ELEMENTS OF MECHANICAL DRAFTING

SAMUEL YASLOW

Instructor, Alexander Hamilton Vocational
and Technical High School
Brooklyn, New York

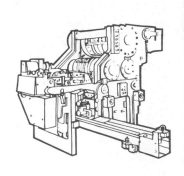

INDUSTRIAL PRESS INC.

200 Madison Ave. New York, N.Y. 10016

The Machinery Publishing Co. Ltd., Brighton, England

CONTENTS

CONTENTS

PREFACE

Elements of Mechanical Drafting has been written as a text for an introductory course in drafting. It explains the ideas, functions, and techniques of mechanical drawing in simple language and is intended for individual student and teacher use in the junior high school industrial arts course and in secondary public and private vocational and academic high schools.

This book has been written to fill the need for a textbook that provides a simple, step-by-step explanation of the well-recognized principles of mechanical drafting and their application to specific problems encountered in the drafting field. These principles have been presented in a series of topical units designed to give the student a firm mastery of the various drafting skills and to assist the teacher in presenting a logical development of the basic information which underlines these skills.

Each unit consists of a series of two-page subject presentations. Each presentation is complete in itself and includes: (1) a new drafting principle, (2) illustrations and explanations showing how this principle is applied, (3) a definite assignment, and (4) step-by-step directions for completing the assignment. This arrangement of subject matter in a graded series of two-page presentations shows each student exactly what he is expected to do, permits him to work on his own job and to proceed with a minimum of assistance according to his own ability.

Units 1 through 3 take up the basic factors which enter into the preparation of a mechanical drawing—the equipment, the basic lines, and the lettering. Units 4 through 7 present three types of drawings—oblique, isometric, and orthogonal—and their usage. Units 8 through 10 present additional elements which enter into a mechanical drawing. Units 9 through 14 explain various geometric and non-geometric constructions and their applications in a mechanical drawing. Units 15 through 21 explain working drawings, their interpretation, and some elements not previously covered which are needed to make a complete working drawing. A brief unit on freehand sketching and one on inking and inking instruments are included. In Units 22 through 24 such machine elements as screw threads, bolts, screws, and nuts, keys, and keyseats and their representation are described in considerable detail. Finally, Unit 25 on assembly and detail drawings completes the text.

It has been the intention of the author to present rules and methods that are applicable to typical procedures in common use in the drafting class and in industry. The original conception materialized during the compilation of a series of practical instruction sheets made up for school use. These sheets were favorably received by the author's own classes and by the classes of other teachers. Their results have proved to be highly satisfactory. Because of these encouraging results and at the request of teachers who have used the material, the text was revised and enriched by the addition of more illustrations, review questions and assignments, and brought together in book form.

Appreciation is extended to the High School Division (Vocational) of the Board of Education of the City of New York for authorization to reprint four projects from the official Machine Shop Course of Study as follows: Wheel Puller, Screwdriver, Ball Peen Hammer, and Layout Punch.

To the Student—Drafting as a Career

Drafting is one of the engineer's most important forms of communication. It is the skill which translates an engineering idea into lines and dimensions on a piece of paper.

Good draftsmen are not "born draftsmen." Training, practice, patience, and attention to detail develop knowledge and skill in drafting.

Let us point out the various steps in the career of a draftsman:

1. *Detailer*

   A detailer makes simple changes in detail and assembly drawings. As greater skill develops, he often makes more complex detail drawings, as well as final drawings from design layouts.

2. *Senior Detailer*

   As a senior detailer the draftsman gets his first contact with the making of design drawings. He draws detail, assembly and installation drawings correctly to scale.

3. *Junior Designer*

   In layout work the draftsman is involved more with actual design. Under the direction of designers he learns some of the techniques.

4. *Designer*

   As he gains experience, the designer works more closely with engineers. His intimate knowledge of machines and the operating principles of mechanisms is a big help in developing the details of any design.

The need for competent draftsmen in engineering will continue to grow in years to come. The author hopes that this book starts you on a career that is both exciting and rewarding.

This Course of Study is Based Largely on
The Mechanical and Machine Drawing Syllabus
of
The University of the State of New York
The State Education Department
Division of Industrial Education
Albany, New York

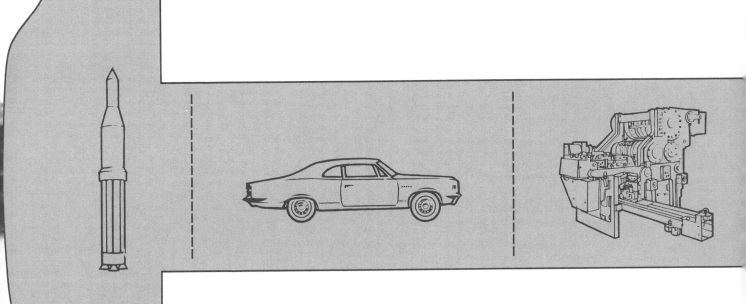

UNIT 1a

EQUIPMENT

The purpose of this unit is to teach the facts about pencils, erasers, T-squares, triangles and scales which one must know in order to use these instruments with understanding and skill. It is also the purpose of this unit to show how to use and care for them properly.

INFORMATION

In order to produce drawings that conform to accepted standards and practices, draftsmen utilize certain types of equipment. A clear understanding of all the drafting tools is important to speed up the process of drawing preparation.

PROBLEM

In your graph notebook, make a list of materials needed. Discuss their cost, use, and place of purchase.

1. Compass
2. Drawing Board
3. T-square
4. 45° and 30°–60° triangles
5. Architect's triangular scale
6. Drawing pencils 6H, 4H, 2H, H, and F
7. Pocket knife and pencil sharpener
8. Pencil pointer (file or sandpaper)
9. Artgum or cleaning rubber
10. Pencil eraser (Ruby)
11. Drafting tape
12. 8½ x 11-inch drawing paper
13. Dusting cloth or brush
14. Graph notebook (with ¼-inch squares)

INSTRUCTIONS

Use 1/8-inch size letters for lettering in your graph notebook. Leave the first page empty for identification purposes.

Drafting Tools	
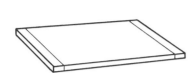 1. Drawing boards, size 18″ x 24″, of soft wood. The left edge of the board should be perfectly straight for guiding the T-square.	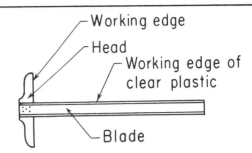 2. The T-square is used for drawing horizontal lines, and also as a guide for triangles in drawing vertical and sloping lines.
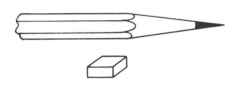 3. Drawing pencils with an F lead for lettering, 2H lead for general use and 4H lead for construction lines are generally used for mechanical drawing. 4. Penciled lines are best erased by means of a medium-soft eraser, using light, firm strokes back and forth.	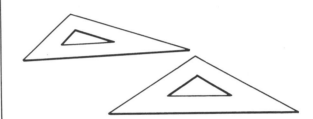 5. Triangles are used for drawing vertical and sloping lines. Those generally used are the 45-degree and the 30—60-degree triangles.
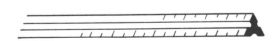 6. The architect's scale has one face subdivided into inches and fractions of an inch: 1/2's, 1/4's, and 1/16's. The remaining five faces are divided into reduced ratios of the full-size scale and are used in making reduced drawings which bear a certain proportion to the full size of the object.	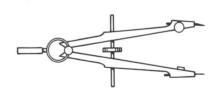 7. The compass is used for drawing circles. The needle point should be adjusted so that it extends about 1/32 inch longer than the pencil point.

Using Drafting Tools Correctly

1. Use the scale only to measure distances. Never draw lines with the scale.

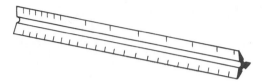

2. Work with a sharp pencil.
   Use the pencil only for its intended purpose. Never put either end of a pencil into your mouth. Never allow any person to force himself against the point of your pencil.

3. Use the T-square as a drawing instrument.

4. Use the *top edge* of the T-square as the working edge. Never draw with the pencil guided against the lower edge of the T-square.

5. Use your portable sharpener and pen knife in a safe manner and only for sharpening your pencil. Store it in an envelope. Do not carry the pen knife with you about the building.

6. Use the compass in a safe manner. Never jab the drawing board, desk top, or any other person with the compass point.

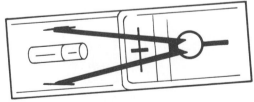

7. Work with clean hands and clean instruments.

Review Questions

Unit 1(a) review questions to be answered on a separate sheet of paper.

DIRECTIONS:

For each of the numbered statements below, write the number and after it the word or words which will complete the sentence. Do NOT write in the book.

1. T-squares are used for drawing ——lines.
   a) slanted
   b) horizontal
   c) angular
   d) vertical
   e) oblique

2. Penciled lines are best erased by a —— soft eraser.
   a) square
   b) medium
   c) light
   d) heavy
   e) rounded

3. Triangles are used for drawing —— and —— lines.
   a) sloping
   b) vertical
   c) horizontal
   d) circular
   e) curved

4. Student draftsmen use a —— scale.
   a) civil engineer's
   b) architect's
   c) flat
   d) mechanical engineer's
   e) electrical

5. The needle point of a compass should extend about —— inch longer than the lead.
   a) 1/16
   b) 1/64
   c) 1/32
   d) 1/8
   e) 3/16

Review Questions (continued)

6. The left side of the drawing board should be perfectly straight so it can be used as a guiding edge for the _____.
   a) triangle
   b) T-square
   c) elbow
   d) pencil
   e) compass

7. Always keep the T-square against the _____.
   a) top of the board
   b) left side of board
   c) bottom of board
   d) front of board
   e) right side of board

8. A triangle has _____.
   a) one angle
   b) two angles
   c) three angles
   d) four angles
   e) five angles

9. Pencils should be kept sharp in order to _____.
   a) center paper
   b) scale
   c) draw fine lines
   d) for appearance
   e) drill

10. The compass is used for drawing _____.
    a) perspective
    b) circles
    c) squares
    d) perpendiculars
    e) letters

THE PENCIL

The purpose of this unit is to teach the use of the pencil.

The most important working tool of the draftsman is the drawing pencil. Many of his tools are employed only occasionally, but the pencil is in almost constant use. It is, therefore, quite essential that the student of drawing be able to select the proper pencils for his use and keep them in a serviceable condition.

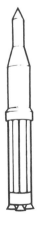

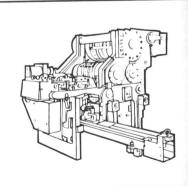

INFORMATION

Grades of drawing pencils:

Drawing pencils are furnished in the following eighteen grades: 7B, 6B, 5B, 4B, 3B, 2B, B, HB, F, H, 2H, 3H, 4H, 5H, 6H, 7H, 8H and 9H. These numbers and letters are stamped upon the pencil and indicate the degree of hardness of the lead, ranging from 7B, which is the softest and blackest, to 9H, which is the hardest.

Drawing pencils are hexagonal in section to prevent them from rolling too easily.

Accuracy of construction is the principal objective of the work in this unit. Accurate work cannot be done with a blunt pencil point. It is important that your pencil point be long and sharply pointed. When drawing, hold the pencil nearly perpendicular to the paper so that the thin point will not be broken.

PROBLEM

In your graph notebook make a list of rules and sketches about the pencil and compass.

INSTRUCTIONS

In your graph notebook, make a list of all the important rules pertaining to the pencil. Lettering should be done freehand, single-stroke, with vertical capitals 1/8 inch high.

Copy sketches and rules for the use of the compass lead. The correct length for a compass lead must be adhered to for perfect results. The only way to maintain a sharp crisp line is to keep the lead well sharpened.

Selecting and Sharpening a Pencil

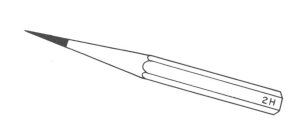

1. Sharpen the unlettered end of the pencil. The hardness or softness grade will then be still visible.

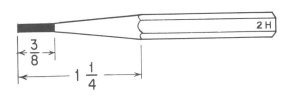

2. First, remove enough of the wood with a razor or knife so that about 1/2 inch of lead is exposed.

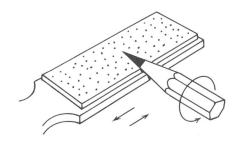

3. Rub the pencil lead across sandpaper and rotate with the fingers at the same time to get a conical point.

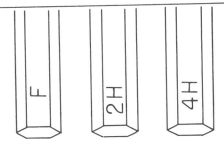

4. Use an F pencil for lettering.
Use a 2H pencil for general use.
Use a 4H pencil construction for lines.

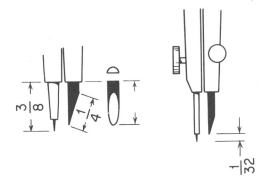

5. Correct length for compass lead and needle point. Notice that the compass lead is sharpened on only one side to a chisel point as shown in 1.13. Use an H lead.

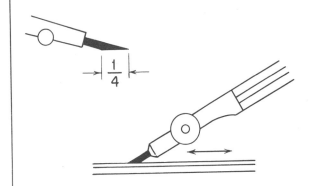

6. Correct way to sharpen the lead of a compass with the sandpaper block.

Review Questions

Unit 1b review questions to be answered on a separate sheet of paper.

DIRECTIONS:

For each of the numbered statements below, write the number and after it the figure, symbol, word or words which will complete the sentence. Do NOT write in the book.

1. Sharpen the _____ end of pencil.
   a) lettered   c) unlettered
   b) smooth   d) rough

2. Remove enough wood with a razor blade or knife to expose about _____ inch of lead.
   a) 1/8   d) 1/2
   b) 1/4   e) 3/16
   c) 3/8

3. Use a/an _____ grade pencil for lettering.
   a) F   d) 6H
   b) 2H   e) HB
   c) 4H

4. A compass lead should project out of the compass _____ inch.
   a) 1/8   d) 5/16
   b) 1/4   e) 11/32
   c) 3/8

5. Rotate the pencil with the fingers when sharpening on a sandpaper block in order to attain a _____ point.
   a) flat   d) chisel
   b) conical   e) round
   c) angular

6. On what parts of a drawing would you use a 2H pencil?

7. The correct length that a compass lead should extend out of the compass is _____.

8. On what parts of a drawing would you use a 4H drawing pencil?

9. Why are pencils made in a hexagonal shape?

10. On what parts of a drawing would you use an F drawing pencil?

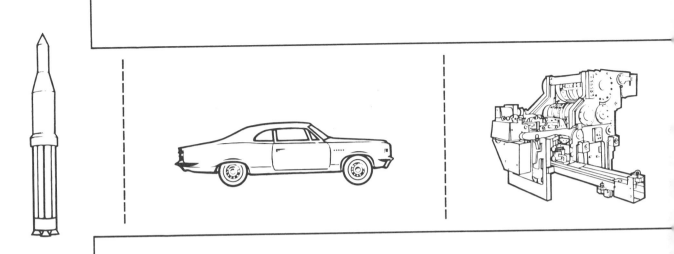

THE DRAWING PAPER

The purpose of this unit is to show how the drawing paper should be placed on and attached to the drafting board.

INFORMATION

This is a demonstration of how to attach the drawing paper to the drawing board.

Since the T-square blade is more rigid near the head than toward the outer end, the paper should be placed close to the left edge of the board. Follow each step carefully because future jobs should be done in the same manner.

Drafting tape is recommended rather than thumbtacks to hold the paper on the board in order to avoid marring the board's surface.

Attaching the Drawing Paper to the Drawing Board

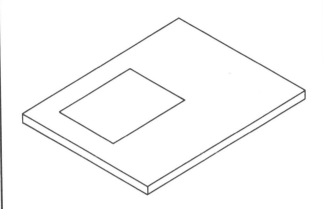

1. Place paper in the upper left hand corner of the drawing board about 2 inches in from the left edge.

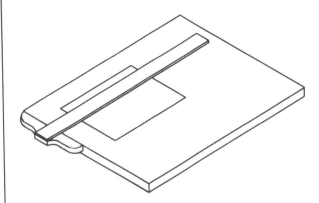

2. Place the T-square on the board with the head firmly against the left edge of the board.

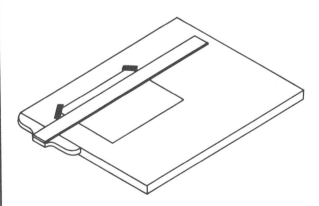

3. Slide the T-square until the blade is in line with the top of the sheet. Move the paper until the edge is parallel with the blade and attach the sheet.

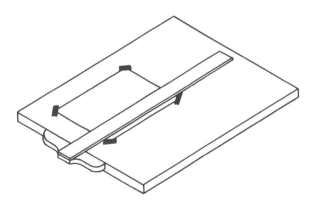

4. Slide the T-square down the paper to remove wrinkles and tape bottom corners.

Review Questions

Unit 1c review questions to be answered on a separate sheet of paper.

DIRECTIONS:

For each of the numbered statements below, write the number and after it the figure, symbol, word or words which will complete the sentence. Do NOT write in the book.

1. When drawing, the head of the T-square is held against the _____ edge of the board.
   a) right
   b) left
   c) middle
   d) slanted
   e) smooth

2. The upper edge of the paper is _____ with the edge of the T-square.
   a) parallel
   b) smooth
   c) perpendicular
   d) oblong
   e) slanted

3. Slide the T-square down the paper to remove _____.
   a) drawing board
   b) paper
   c) wrinkles
   d) erasures
   e) dust

4. Slide the T-square until the blade is in line with the _____ of the sheet.
   a) back
   b) side
   c) front
   d) top
   e) left

5. The drawing paper is attached on all four sides with _____.
   a) clips
   b) paste
   c) glue
   d) tape
   e) thumbtacks

Review Questions (continued)

6. Paper is placed in the upper _____ corner of the drawing board.
   a) left-hand
   b) right-hand
   c) diagonal-end
   d) offset
   e) straight

7. Against which end of the board should the head of the T-square be placed?
   a) right
   b) left
   c) bottom
   d) top
   e) horizontal

8. T-squares are a guide for triangles in drawing _____ lines.
   a) left
   b) vertical
   c) horizontal
   d) right
   e) side

9. Use adhesive drafting tape to _____ the paper to the board.
   a) clean
   b) warm
   c) hold
   d) crease
   e) draw

10. Use only the _____ edge of the blade of a T-square as a ruling guide.
    a) right
    b) left
    c) upper
    d) middle
    e) side

BEGINNING TO DRAW

The purpose of this unit is to show how horizontal, vertical and slanting lines are drawn by using the T-square and triangles and how the border lines and title block of a drawing are laid out.

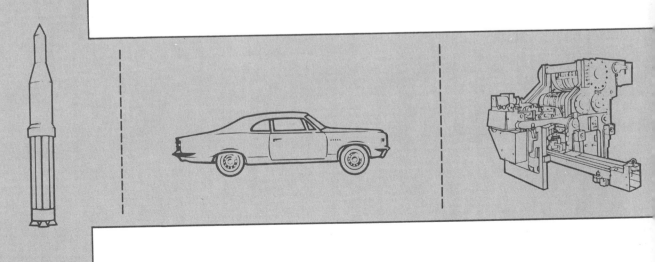

INFORMATION

Every drafting room has its own standard form of title block. Words in the title block should be lettered freehand with single-stroke vertical capitals in the sizes specified.

PROBLEM

In your graph notebook, copy the sketches showing the use of the T-square and triangle, and the layout of the title block.

INSTRUCTIONS

In your graph notebook, draw a sketch of *vertical* lines being drawn with the triangle set against the T-square and with the perpendicular edge of the triangle nearest the head of the square.

In your graph notebook, draw a sketch of the T-square being used to draw *horizontal* lines with its head against the left edge of the drawing board.

To lay out the title block proceed in the following order:

1. Having placed the paper on the board, lay out the standard border line and title space. Take the measurements with your scale, first horizontally, and rule in the vertical lines lightly with a 6H pencil.
2. Take the vertical measurements and rule in the horizontal lines.
3. Letter in the title block subdivisions as shown on page 19.
4. Now go over the entire layout with an H pencil, making the lines black and firm.

Drawing Horizontal and Vertical Lines

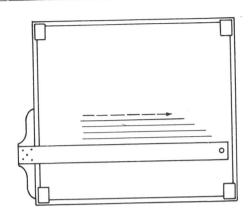

The T-square is used for drawing horizontal lines from left to right.

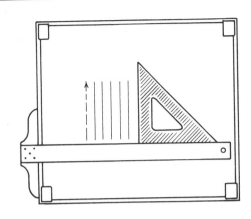

The triangle is used in combination with the T-square for drawing vertical lines.

Drawing a Title Block

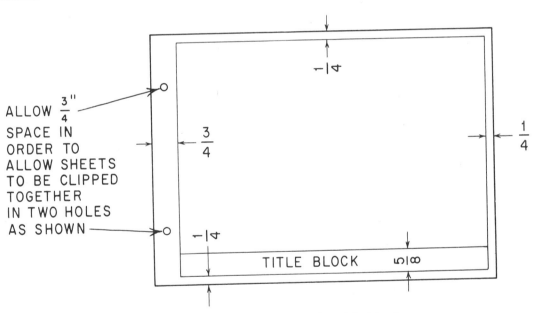

ALLOW $\frac{3}{4}$" SPACE IN ORDER TO ALLOW SHEETS TO BE CLIPPED TOGETHER IN TWO HOLES AS SHOWN

$\frac{1}{4}$

$\frac{3}{4}$

$\frac{1}{4}$

$\frac{1}{4}$

TITLE BLOCK $\frac{5}{8}$

Dimensions for title block.

5 – $\frac{1}{8}$ inch spaces

Namplate

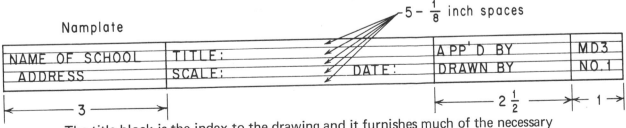

| NAME OF SCHOOL | TITLE: | | APP'D BY | MD3 |
| ADDRESS | SCALE: | DATE: | DRAWN BY | NO. 1 |

3   2 $\frac{1}{2}$ 1

The title block is the index to the drawing and it furnishes much of the necessary information. Title blocks are almost always placed in the lower right-hand corner of the drawing.

INFORMATION

Lines may be drawn at 45 degrees either to the right or to the left, and at 90 degrees to the horizontal, with a 45-degree triangle as shown on page 21.

Lines may be drawn at 30 degrees or 60 degrees to the right or left, and at 90 degrees to the horizontal, with the 30-60-degree triangle as shown on page 21.

Lines at 15 degrees and 75 degrees to the horizontal may be drawn by combining the two triangles as shown on page 21.

Parallel lines may be drawn with T-square or with the T-square and triangle as shown on page 22.

Lines may be drawn at right angles (perpendicular) to slanting lines with the T-square and triangle as shown on page 22.

PROBLEM

Copy the sketches showing the use of triangles separately and in combination.

INSTRUCTIONS

1. Draw border lines and title block. Divide the enclosed space into eight boxes as shown. Copy angles shown on page 21 using triangles separately and in combination.
2. Draw border lines and title block. Divide the enclosed space into six boxes and copy parallel and perpendicular lines shown on page 22.

Drawing Slanting Lines with T-square and Triangle

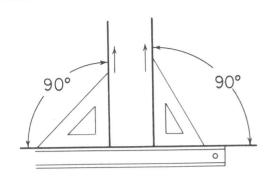
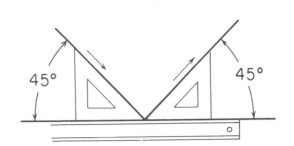

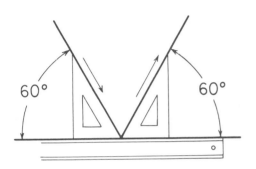
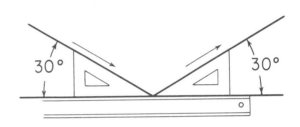

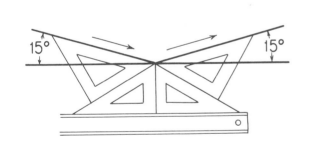
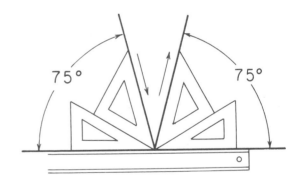

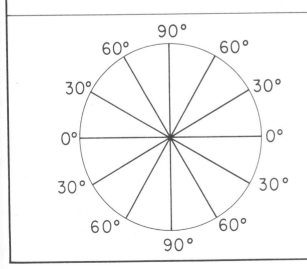
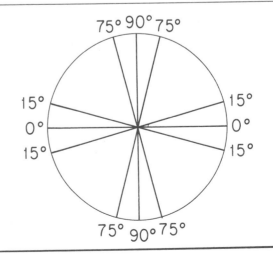

Drawing Parallel and Perpendicular Lines with T-square and Triangle

1. Horizontal parallel lines

2. Vertical parallel lines

90°

Perpendicular

Parallel

3. 60-degree lines from the horizontal

90°

Perpendicular

Parallel

4. 30-degree lines from the horizontal

90°

Perpendicular

Parallel

5. 45-degree lines from the horizontal

90°

Perpendicular

Parallel

6. Any given position

Review Questions

Unit 1d review questions to be answered on a separate sheet of paper.

DIRECTIONS

For each of the numbered statements below, write the number and after it the word which will complete the sentence. Do NOT write in the book.

1. Triangles are used for drawing _____ lines.
   - a) light
   - b) curved
   - c) vertical
   - d) horizontal
   - e) elliptical

2. T-squares are used for drawing _____ lines.
   - a) curved
   - b) sloping
   - c) elliptical
   - d) horizontal
   - e) vertical

3. The title block is the _____ to the drawing.
   - a) answer
   - b) design
   - c) index
   - d) detail
   - e) assembly

4. A horizontal line is one which is level, or parallel with the _____.
   - a) plane
   - b) offset
   - c) circle
   - d) horizon
   - e) vertical

5. A vertical line is one which is perpendicular to a/an _____ line.
   - a) plane
   - b) offset
   - c) horizontal
   - d) sloping
   - e) parallel

Review Questions (continued)

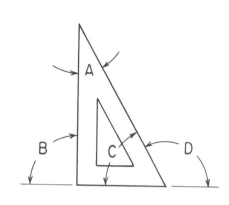

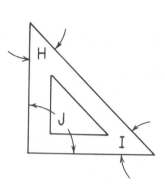

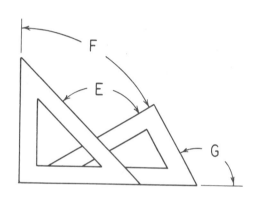

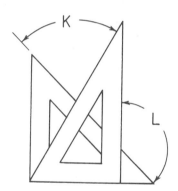

On a separate sheet of paper write the angle letters as shown below and after each write the corresponding number of degrees as determined from the diagrams above. Do NOT write in the book.

A _____   G _____

B _____   H _____

C _____   I _____

D _____   J _____

E _____   K _____

F _____   L _____

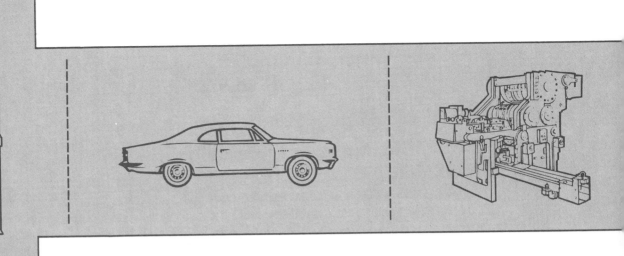

UNIT 2a

LINES

The purpose of this unit is to provide practice in the drawing of lines. To prepare an acceptable drawing a draftsman must use lines that are even in weight and in width. They must be located accurately and be carefully joined.

INFORMATION

In the following exercises, the aim should be for accuracy of measurement and drawing. Even in these first exercises, no line should vary from its specified position as much as 1/64 inch. The lines should be thin but firm. The enclosing rectangle should always be made first and then the pattern constructed within it. Whenever one line terminates upon another, care should be exercised to draw exactly up to that line but not over it.

PROBLEM

Make the line drawing shown, as a progressive exercise for practice in the use of the pencil for drawing lines.

INSTRUCTIONS

Draw border lines and title block. Center drawing on paper. Draw to the dimensions shown with the T-square and triangles. Use a 2H pencil with a conical point.

Line-drawing Practice—1

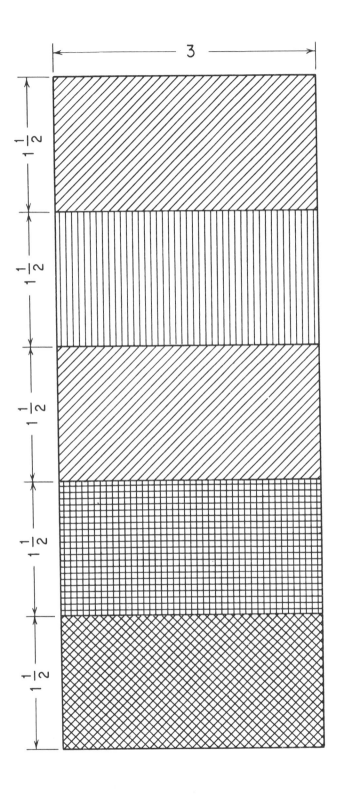

INFORMATION

This job is a continuation of the previous one for practice in the use of the pencil in drawing lines.

PROBLEM

Make a pencil rendering of the two drawings to dimensions specified.

INSTRUCTIONS

Draw border lines and title block. With a vertical line divide paper into two equal parts. In the left-hand part draw a 3 1/4-inch square box. Then draw the horizontal and vertical lines to make the pattern shown. Use the T-square for all horizontal lines and a triangle with the T-square for all vertical lines. Use a 2H pencil for line work. Omit dimensions.

In the right-hand part draw a 3 1/4-inch square box. Divide the box with horizontal and vertical lines to the dimensions shown. Then erase the portions of the lines not shown. Omit dimensions.

Darken the outline of both boxes with a heavy line.

Line-drawing Practice—2

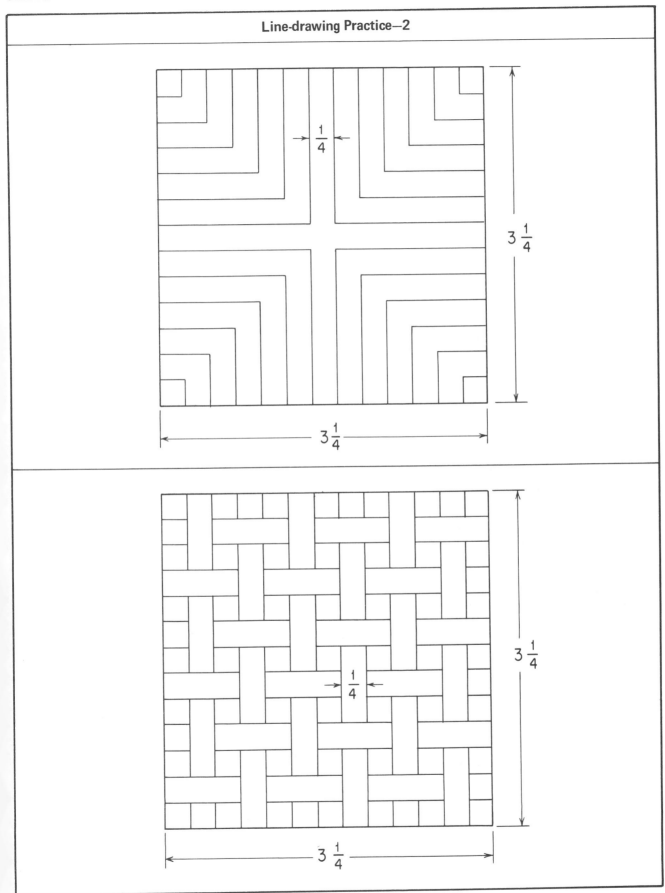

Review Questions

Unit 2a review questions to be answered on a separate sheet of paper.

DIRECTIONS

For each of the numbered statements below, write the number and after it the word or symbol which will complete the sentence. Do NOT write in the book.

1. A horizontal line is one which is level, or parallel with the _____.
   a) angle
   b) vertical
   c) horizon
   d) slope
   e) oblique

2. A sloping line is one which is neither horizontal nor _____.
   a) perpendicular
   b) parallel
   c) conical
   d) vertical
   e) circular

3. Parallel lines are a/an _____ distance apart throughout their entire length.
   a) short
   b) long
   c) furthest
   d) equal
   e) many

4. We use a/an _____ lead in a compass.
   a) 2H
   b) H
   c) HB
   d) 4H
   e) 6H

5. Use _____ lead for line exercises.
   a) HB
   b) H
   c) 2H
   d) F
   e) 6H

CIRCLES AND ARCS

The purpose of this unit is to teach the use and care of the compass and to show how to make certain geometric constructions which are used in mechanical drawing and which require the use of compasses.

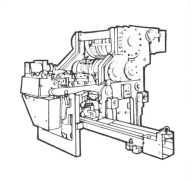

INFORMATION

The compass is used for drawing circles and arcs of circles. The small compass, generally called a bow compass, is used for the smaller circles, up to about 1¼ inches in radius. The large compass is used from the limit of the small compass up to circles having a radius of about 7 inches.

The compass should be held by the knurled handle and tipped slightly in the direction of motion. Revolution should be clockwise. Allow only the weight of the compass to bear down upon the needle point, as greater pressure will cause the point to wear a hole in the paper, thus causing inaccurate work.

PROBLEM

Make a sketch of the circle and its parts in your graph notebook.

INSTRUCTIONS

Print the definition for each sketch with a soft pencil. Draw the letters 1/8-inch high.

The Circle and its Parts

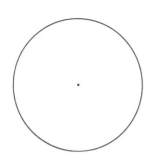

1. A circle is a closed curved line called the circumference, every point on which is equally distant from an inner point called the center.

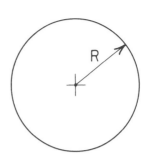

2. The radius is any straight line going from the center to the circumference of the circle.

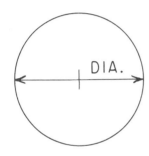

3. The diameter is any straight line passing from one side to the other through the center of the circle. The diameter of a given circle has twice the length of the radius.

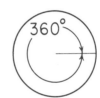

4. There are 360 degrees in a circle and 180 degrees in a half circle. Half a circle is called a semi-circle.

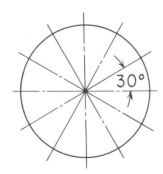

5. When a circle is divided into 12 parts, each angle equals 30 degrees.

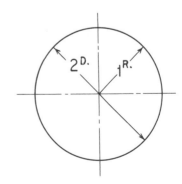

6. Dimension a circle as shown.

INFORMATION

In using the compass, the needle point should not be pushed through the paper, although where many concentric circles are to be drawn, this cannot be entirely avoided. However, it is unnecessary to make large unsightly holes at the center of any circle or series of circles.

PROBLEM

Make the drawing shown, as a progressive exercise in the use of the compass for drawing circles and arcs.

INSTRUCTIONS

Draw border lines and title block. Center drawing on paper. Draw with a compass having an H lead in its chuck. Draw the circular pattern to dimensions shown.

Using the Compass—1

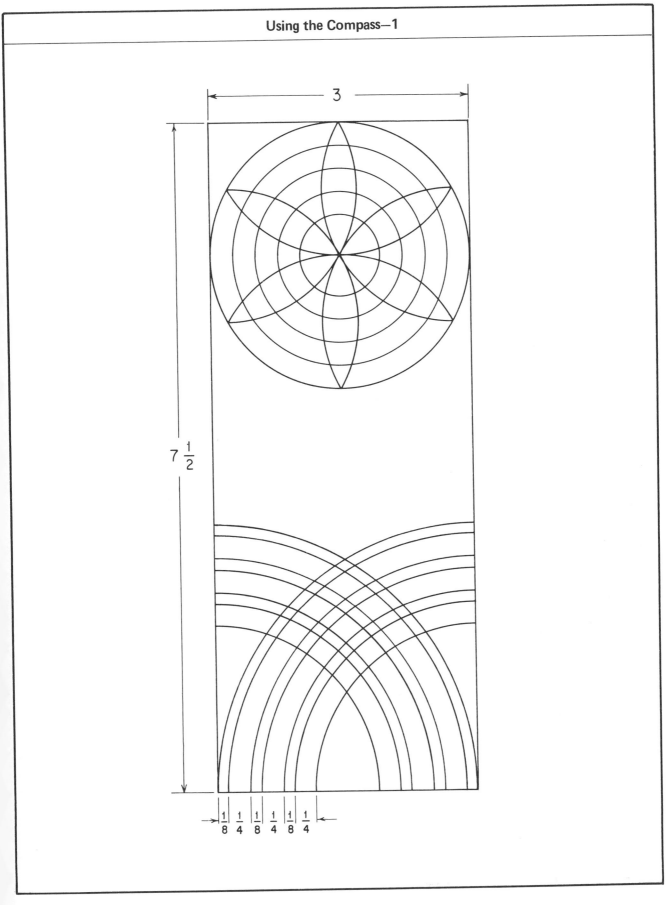

INFORMATION

This job is an exercise in using the compass. By using an H lead in the compass and continually sharpening it with a sandpaper block, you can ensure a sharp, crisp, thin, dark line.

PROBLEM

Draw the circle patterns shown.

INSTRUCTIONS

1. Draw border lines and title block.
2. With a vertical line divide enclosed space into two equal parts.
3. Locate the center of the circular pattern in the left-hand space by lightly drawing with a 6H pencil two diagonal lines from corner to corner and using the intersecting point as the center. Draw the circular pattern.
4. In the right-hand space locate the center of the largest circle and using a 2H lead draw this circle and the two smaller circles having the same center.
5. Draw two center lines at right angles to each other with a 4H pencil.
6. Using a 6H lead lightly draw the 3-inch diameter circle on which the centers of the 12 small circles lie.
7. Set the dividers to the radius of this circle and starting at the intersection of one of the center lines and this circle step off six centers for the 5/8-inch diameter holes. Then, starting at the intersection of the other center line with the 3-inch diameter circle, step-off the remaining six 5/8-inch diameter holes.
8. Using a compass draw in the twelve 5/8-inch diameter holes.

Practice in Drawing Circles

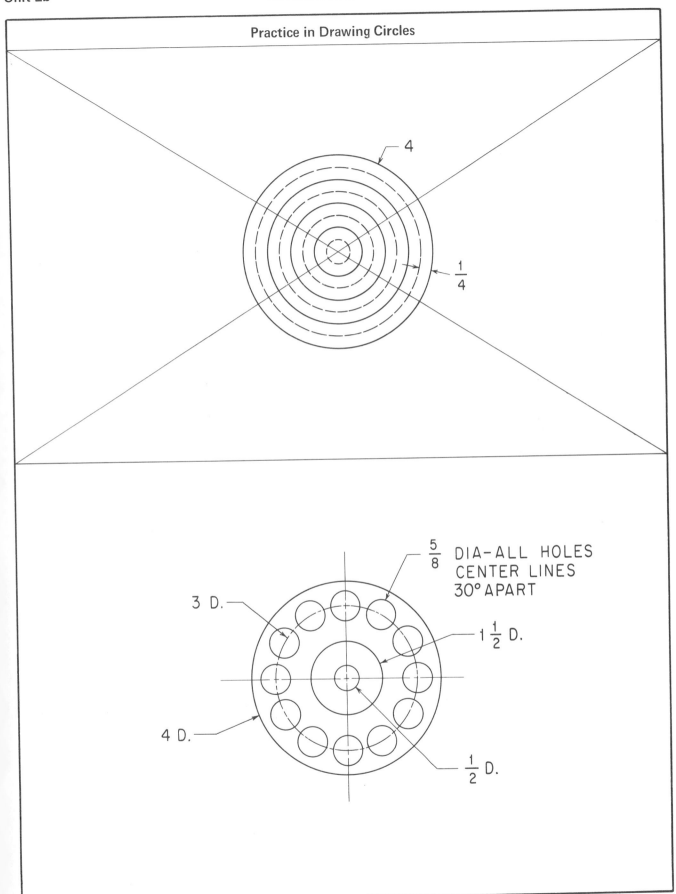

DIRECTIONS

For each of the numbered statements below, write the number and after it the word or words which will complete the sentence if placed in the blank space provided. Do NOT write in the book. Write all answers on a separate sheet of paper.

1. A _____ is a closed curved line on a plane where every part is an equal distance from a point within, called the center.
   a) square
   b) rectangle
   c) polygon
   d) circle
   e) triangle

2. The radius is a _____ line from the center to the circle.
   a) curved
   b) crooked
   c) free form
   d) straight
   e) dimension

3. The _____ is the distance around the circle.
   a) radius
   b) arc
   c) circumference
   d) diameter
   e) curve

4. An arc is a part of a _____.
   a) square
   b) rectangle
   c) pyramid
   d) circle
   e) radius

5. What should be the difference in length of projection between the needle point and pencil point?
   a) 1/64 inch
   b) 1/32 inch
   c) 1/8 inch
   d) 3/16 inch
   e) 1/4 inch

6. How should the lead in the compass be sharpened?
   a) short
   b) bevelled
   c) long
   d) conical
   e) chiseled

7. A _____ is used for drawing circles, and arcs of circles.
   a) ruler
   b) compass
   c) protractor
   d) divider
   e) center line

8. A semi-circle has _____ degrees.
   a) 30
   b) 60
   c) 90
   d) 45
   e) 180

9. Each part of a circle which is divided into 12 parts equals _____ degrees.
   a) 30
   b) 60
   c) 90
   d) 45
   e) 180

10. A circle is dimensioned by its _____.
    a) chord
    b) radius
    c) diameter
    d) frame
    e) tangent

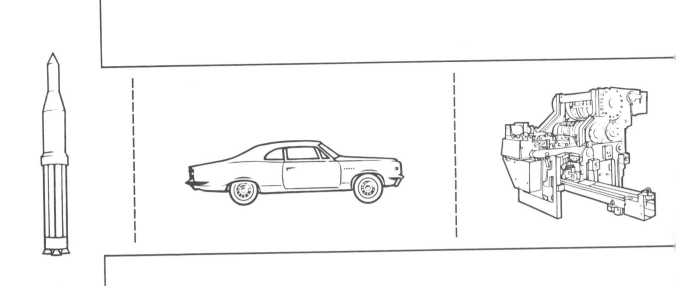

UNIT 3

LETTERING

The purpose of this unit is to teach certain important facts about the shapes, heights, sizes, slopes, and weights of letters and numbers, and to show how to draw letters and numbers.

INFORMATION

The first step in the development of good lettering is a thorough and correct knowledge of the standard letter shapes. Such knowledge may be acquired through the study of each of the letters, the correct proportions of which are shown in the figures in this unit. The direction in which each stroke should be made is shown on each letter, and the important points of each letter are discussed in the paragraphs which follow. These should be studied carefully until each letter can be made from memory exactly as shown in the text.

PROBLEM

Draw Gothic vertical capital letters in your graph notebook. Add the direction of strokes as shown in the figures.

INSTRUCTIONS

In the graph notebook, draw the letters 1/4-inch in height with a soft H pencil.

Elements of Lettering

The first rule in lettering is to make it legible (readable) and understandable.

If you try some straight line letters, you'll find that each line is easily drawn from the top down and from the left toward the right. For example:

If you try to draw the strokes in the opposite direction, it becomes akward.

When a letter contains a circle or arc, we follow the same rule. We draw from the top down, and from the left to the right. For example:

Numbers are drawn in the same way. For example:

Rules for Lettering

1. Lettering will be drawn in capitals having uniform height.
2. Beginners learning the shape and spacing of letters will draw them between light horizontal lines, 1/8 inch apart.
3. The spaces between letters will be approximately one-sixth of their height.
4. The spaces between words will equal the width of one regular letter.
5. The spaces between sentences will equal the width of two letters.
6. Punctuation marks will be separated from the preceding word by one-sixth and from the following word by two-thirds the height of one letter.
7. Lettering will be underlined <u>for emphasis only</u>.
8. Whole numbers will be the height of accompanying letters.
   Example: NUMBER 5
9. Common fractions will be five-eighths the height of the accompanying whole numbers.
10. Neither the numerator nor denominator of a common fraction will touch the bar separating them.
   Example: $\frac{1}{2}$ not $\frac{1}{2}$

INFORMATION

Industry requires that draftsmen have the ability to letter uniformly, rapidly, and legibly. If you are planning to enter industry as a draftsman, technician, or engineer, you will find it to your advantage to develop this ability.

Anyone can develop the ability if he is willing to practice with sincere effort and "stick-to-itiveness," although some students will need more practice than others.

PROBLEM

Draw Gothic, vertical, capital letters in propor proportions, as shown.

INSTRUCTIONS

Draw border lines and title block. Divide the enclosed space into eight equal parts. In the first part, draw the simple straight-line letters in their proper proportions. Center letters in the space provided. Use a 4H pencil for construction lines and then darken each letter with a well-sharpened H pencil. Repeat the same procedure for drawing all the other letters shown on page 45.

Drawing Gothic Capital Letters

UNITS

Simple

Diagonals

Symmetrical

Single-ovals

Half-ovals

Double-ovals

Exceptions:

Very wide

Good spacing
Note: six units between words

Review Questions

Unit 3 review questions to be answered on a separate sheet of paper.

DIRECTIONS:
    For each of the numbered statements below, write the number and after it the figure, symbol, word or words which will complete the sentence. Do NOT write in the book.

1. Draw _____ capital letters.
   a) Roman
   b) Gothic
   c) script
   d) square
   e) lower case

2. Use a/an _____ lead pencil for lettering.
   a) 2H
   b) 5F
   c) F
   d) 3H
   e) 4H

3. Letter strokes are from the _____ down.
   a) top
   b) side
   c) left
   d) right
   e) middle

4. An "O" is an example of a/an _____ oval.
   a) half
   b) single
   c) double
   d) round
   e) circular

5. The widest letter in the alphabet is _____.
   a) A
   b) B
   c) W
   d) M
   e) T

6. Lettering is done with a pencil having a _____ point.
   a) sharp
   b) dull
   c) slightly round edge
   d) conical
   e) chisel edge

7. The first rule in lettering is to make it _____.
   a) square
   b) straight
   c) legible
   d) round
   e) slanted

8. The height of letters used in notes on drawings is _____ inch.
   a) 3/16
   b) 1/8
   c) 3/32
   d) 1/4
   e) 1/16

9. Keep the guide lines for lettering _____.
   a) very light
   b) light
   c) medium
   d) heavy
   e) dark

10. The most important requirement for lettering is to be able to letter _____.
    a) easily
    b) clearly
    c) rapidly
    d) neatly
    e) lightly

OBLIQUE DRAWING

The purpose of a pictorial drawing is to show the general location, function, and appearance of parts and assemblies. There are two common types of pictorial views drawn by draftsmen: (1) the isometric, (2) the oblique.

One-view pictorial drawings are being more widely used each year. Although they look like a picture, one need not be an artist to make a pictorial drawing. In fact, a pictorial drawing is made with the regular drawing tools.

INFORMATION

The purpose of this unit is to teach the use of pictorial drawings and to show how to make oblique drawings.

How many times have you wanted to explain an idea and tried to draw a picture? Whether you will be a carpenter, a machinist, or a printer, you will be called on occasionally to clarify an idea by making a drawing.

One of the easiest drawings to produce is the oblique drawing.

In an oblique drawing, the front face of the object is shown in its true size and shape as if it were in a true view drawing, and the receding lines of the other two sides are drawn obliquely at any angle, usually 45 degrees to the horizontal.

PROBLEM

Make an oblique drawing of the steel block shown on page 51.

INSTRUCTIONS

1. Draw border lines and title block.
2. With a vertical line divide the enclosed space into two parts.
3. In the first part, draw the steel block shown on page 51, in oblique projection. Center the view in the space provided.
4. In the second part, the figure shown on page 53 will be drawn later.
5. Use a sharp F pencil for object lines and a sharp 4H pencil for construction lines. (Do not erase construction lines.) Omit hidden lines unless necessary for clearness of some feature on the back side.
6. Start oblique drawings with a true front view and draw receding lines at 45 degrees with the horizontal. Repeat the procedure for other oblique views.

Making an Oblique Drawing—1

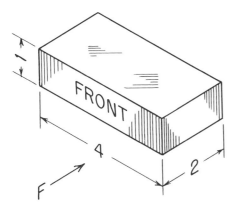

STEEL BLOCK

1. Select the front face and draw it in the front view.

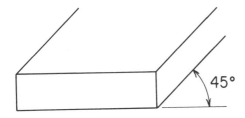

2. From each corner on the top and right edges, project light lines at 45 degrees with the horizontal.

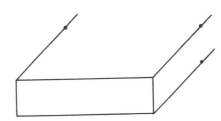

3. On each of these lines, measure off the width.

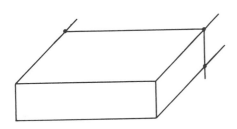

4. Connect the points.

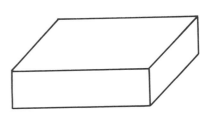

5. Darken all object lines.

INFORMATION

This is a one-view pictorial drawing based on the theoretical principle that the front face of the object is placed parallel to the picture plane. Oblique projectors extend from the corners to the rear face of the object. These projectors may make any angle less than 90 degrees with the horizontal. This type of drawing can thus be called an oblique projection drawing.

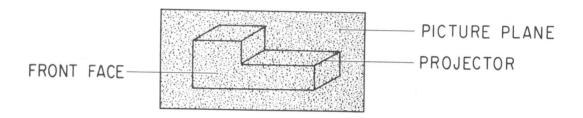

PROBLEM

Make an oblique drawing of the L-block shown above.

INSTRUCTIONS

Draw the figure in the second half of the oblique drawing sheet used for the previous drawing.

Making an Oblique Drawing—2

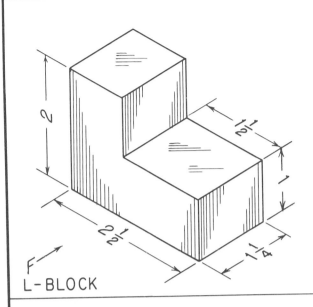

L-BLOCK

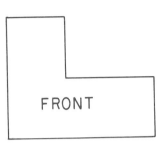

FRONT

1. Select the front face and draw it in the front view.

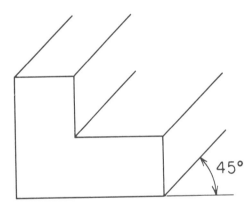

2. From each corner on the top and right edges project light lines at 45 degrees.

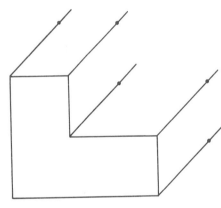

3. On each of these lines measure off the width.

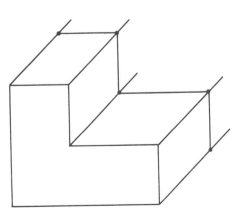

4. Connect the points.

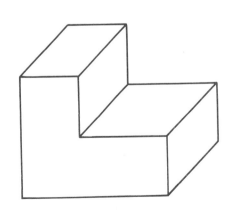

5. Darken all object lines.

INFORMATION

It is important to center a drawing on a sheet of paper. This indicates that you are planning ahead and it shows careful thought. Good professional presentation enhances a job.

PROBLEM

Center the drawing of a steel block in an oblique view within a given space on a sheet of paper.

INSTRUCTIONS

1. Draw border lines and title block. Follow the step-by-step procedure given on the following page in order to center the drawing of the object.

2. Determine the location of the starting point of the drawing.

3. Enough room must be left for dimensions and notes.

4. Every drawing should be well-centered.

Centering an Oblique Drawing

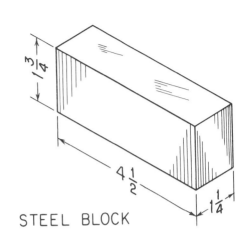

STEEL BLOCK

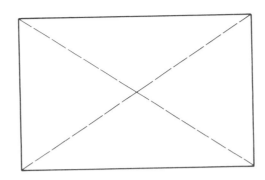

1. Find the center of the sheet by drawing two light diagonal lines.

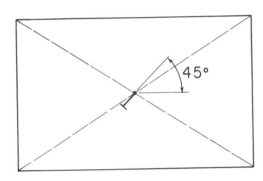

2. Draw from the center point downward to the left on a 45-degree diagonal line (in this case 45° is being used), a distance equal to one-half the depth of the object.

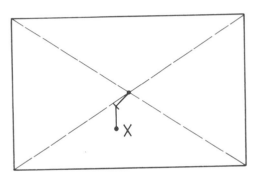

3. From this point, draw directly down a distance equal to one half of the height of the object. X is the center of the bottom edge of the oblique drawing.

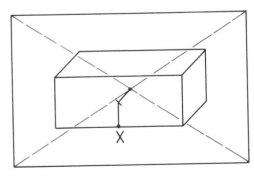

4. From point X, complete the drawing of the object.

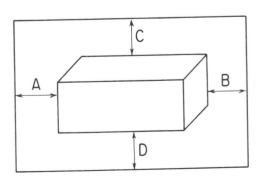

5. Checking: Distances A and B are equal, and C and D are equal.

PROBLEM

Make an oblique drawing of the bevelled block shown on the following page.

INSTRUCTIONS

1. Draw border lines and title block.

2. Center the oblique drawing on the sheet of paper.

Making an Oblique Drawing—3

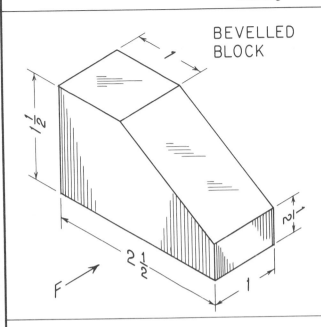

BEVELLED
BLOCK

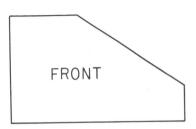

FRONT

1. Select the front face and draw it in the front view.

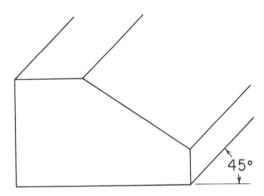

45°

2. From each corner on the top and right edges project light lines at 45 degrees with the horizontal.

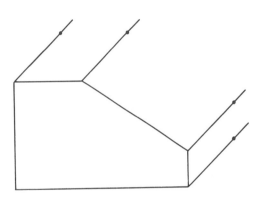

3. On each of these lines measure the width.

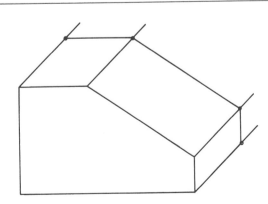

4. Connect the points.

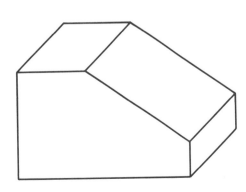

5. Darken all object lines and erase unwanted lines.

INFORMATION

Oblique drawing has one great advantage over isometric drawing in that circles, arcs, and irregular contours may be represented in their true shapes in one face. For this reason, the object should always be placed so that circles or irregular contours will face the front.

PROBLEM

Draw an oblique view of the cylinder shown on the following page.

INSTRUCTIONS

1. Draw border lines and title block.

2. Use the step-by-step method for guidance in drawing the oblique cylinder.

Making an Oblique Drawing—4

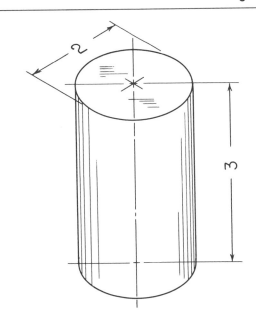

1. Draw a complete circle as a front view.

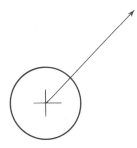

2. Project the center back at 45°.

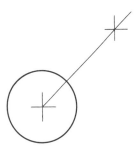

3. Measure the length on the center line.

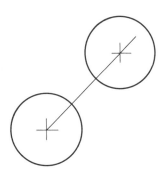

4. Draw the second circle.

5. Draw the sides of the cylinder and darken the entire outline.

PROBLEM

Make oblique drawings from the isometric drawings shown on the following page.

INSTRUCTIONS

1. Draw border lines and title block. Divide paper into two equal parts.

2. In the first part, make an oblique drawing of the L-block.

3. In the second part, make an oblique drawing of the T-block.

4. Repeat this procedure on a second sheet for the step block and the corner block.

5. Repeat this procedure on a third sheet for the two-edge blocks.

Making an Oblique Drawing—5

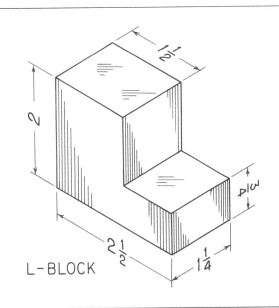

L–BLOCK

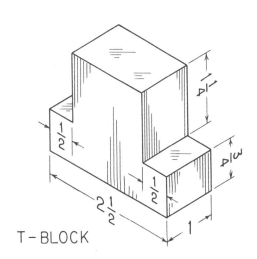

T–BLOCK

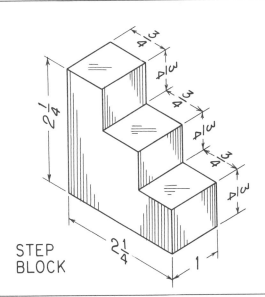

STEP BLOCK

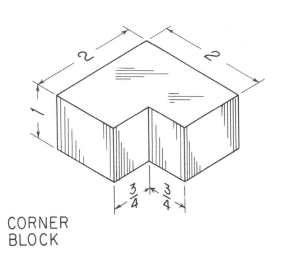

CORNER BLOCK

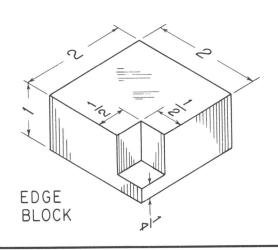

EDGE BLOCK

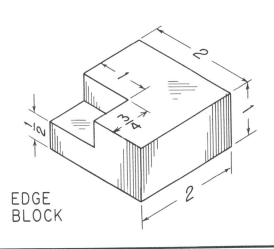

EDGE BLOCK

Review Questions

Unit 4 review questions to be answered on a separate sheet of paper.

DIRECTIONS:

For each of the numbered statements below, write the number and after it the figure, symbol, word or words which will complete the sentence. Do NOT write in the book.

1. In an oblique drawing the _____ face is in its true size.
   a) front
   b) right side
   c) top
   d) left side
   e) bottom

2. The angle used in an oblique drawing is usually _____ degrees.
   a) 30
   b) 60
   c) 45
   d) 90
   e) 180

3. The word oblique means _____.
   a) horizontal
   b) slanted
   c) similar
   d) straight
   e) round

4. An oblique drawing is a _____ drawing.
   a) perspective
   b) pictorial
   c) pencil
   d) working
   e) colored

5. In an oblique drawing the vertical lines are _____.
   a) slanted
   b) parallel
   c) angular
   d) perpendicular
   e) tangent

6. Receding lines in an oblique drawing are drawn _____ to the axis.
   a) close
   b) near
   c) parallel
   d) oblique
   e) perpendicular

7. In an oblique drawing, circles are represented in their _____ shape in the front view.
   a) angular
   b) large
   c) small
   d) typical
   e) true

8. Construction lines are drawn with a/an _____ pencil.
   a) H
   b) F
   c) 4H
   d) 3H
   e) 6H

9. It is customary to draw the receding lines of an oblique drawing at _____ degrees with the horizontal.
   a) 30
   b) 60
   c) 90
   d) 45
   e) 120

10. An oblique drawing is a _____ view pictorial drawing.
    a) one
    b) two
    c) three
    d) four
    e) five

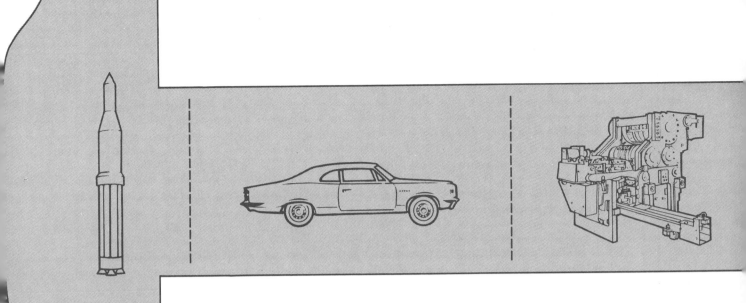

UNIT 5

ISOMETRIC DRAWING

The purpose of this unit is to teach the use of pictorial drawings and particularly to show how to make isometric drawings.

Drawings that show objects somewhat as they would appear in a photograph are called pictorial drawings. The most common of these are known as isometric drawings. An isometric drawing is a good example of the saying "One picture is worth a thousand words".

INFORMATION

The importance of the beginning mechanical drawing student developing the ability to make an isometric drawing CANNOT BE OVER-EMPHASIZED. This ability will serve as a valuable tool in solving drawings based upon the rules of Orthographic Projection.

In an isometric drawing, all lines that are parallel on the object are also parallel on the drawing. Vertical lines on the object are shown in a vertical position. However, horizontal lines on the object are drawn at an angle of 30 degrees with the horizontal. Note that the front face of the isometric drawing is *not* drawn parallel with the picture plane as it is in the oblique drawing.

It should also be noted that all lengths laid out on the isometric axes are true lengths. Thus, the word "isometric" can be broken down to mean:

iso = equal and metric = measure.

PROBLEM

Make isometric drawings of the steel block shown on the following page.

INSTRUCTIONS

1. Draw border lines and title block. Divide the sheet into two parts. In the first part, draw the steel block.

2. Draw thirty-degree, and vertical "light" construction or "axis" lines, as shown.

3. Use a sharp F pencil for object lines and a sharp 4H pencil for construction lines. (Do not erase construction lines.) Omit hidden lines unless necessary for clearness in showing some feature on the back side.

4. Start all isometric drawings at a given corner point. For all problems, study carefully the method of constructing the two 30-degree angles shown here.

Making an Isometric Drawing—1

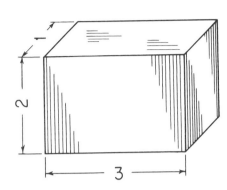

STEEL BLOCK

1. Place a dot in the center of the paper.

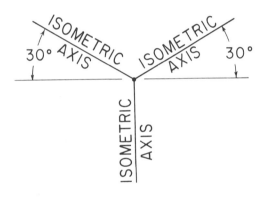

2. Draw three isometric axes.

3. Measure off length, width and height on the respective axes.

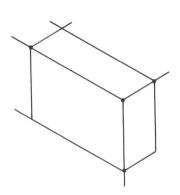

4. Draw lines parallel to axes.

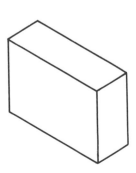

5. Darken all object lines.

PROBLEM

Make an isometric drawing from the oblique drawing of the stepped block shown on the following page.

INSTRUCTIONS

1. Draw border lines and title block.

2. Use the step-by-step method to draw the stepped block in isometric projection.

Making an Isometric Drawing—2

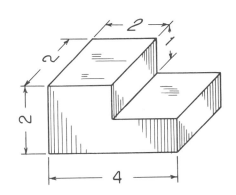

STEPPED BLOCK

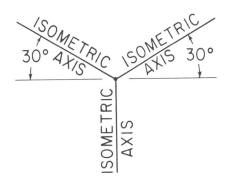

1. Draw three isometric axes.

2. Measure off length, width and height on respective axes.

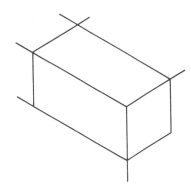

3. Draw lines parallel to axes.

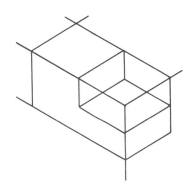

4. Measure off and draw corner cutout.

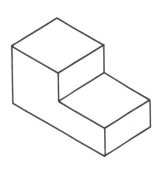

5. Darken all object lines.

INFORMATION

Centering the drawing of an object shows careful planning. The view must not only fit a given space but be properly located within it.

PROBLEM

Center the drawing of a steel block drawn in isometric projection within a given space on a sheet of paper.

INSTRUCTIONS

1. Draw border lines and title block.

2. Determine the location of the starting point of the drawing.

3. Enough room must be left for dimensions and notes.

4. Every drawing should be well centered.

How to Center an Isometric Drawing

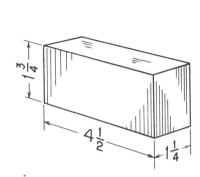

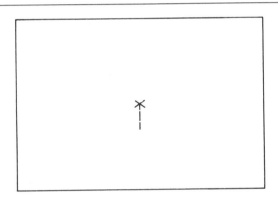

1. Find the center of the working area by drawing two diagonal lines from corner to corner.

2. Determine length, width & height of the object. Measure down one-half the height of the object.

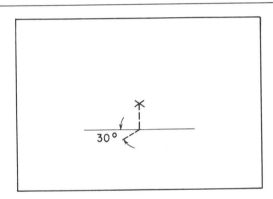

3. Measure one-half the width and construct a 30° line to the left.

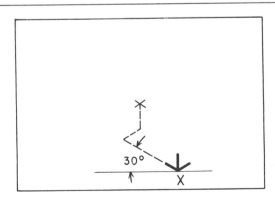

4. Measure one-half the length and construct a 30° line to the right to point X. Construct the isometric axis at this point.

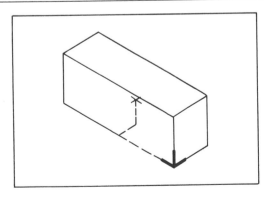

5. Now complete the construction of the isometric drawing.

PROBLEM

Make an isometric drawing of each of the objects shown on the following page.

INSTRUCTIONS

1. Draw border lines and title block.

2. Divide the first sheet into two equal parts.
   a. In the first part, draw the channel block.
   b. In the second part, draw the first grooved block.

3. Divide the second sheet into two equal parts.
   a. In the first part, draw the second grooved block.
   b. In the second part, draw the support.

4. Divide the third sheet into two equal parts.
   a. In the first part, draw the slide.
   b. In the second part, draw the stand.

Making an Isometric Drawing—3

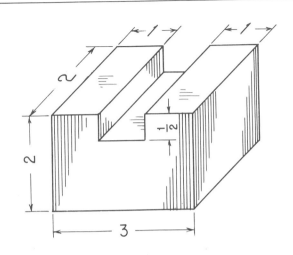

CHANNEL BLOCK

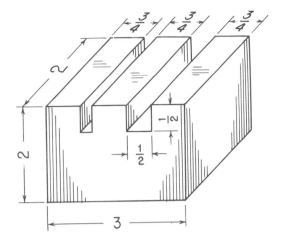

GROOVED BLOCK

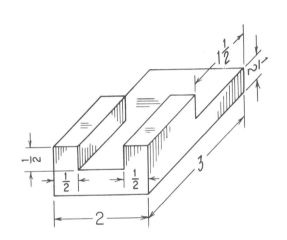

GROOVED BLOCK

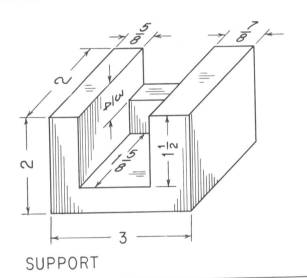

SUPPORT

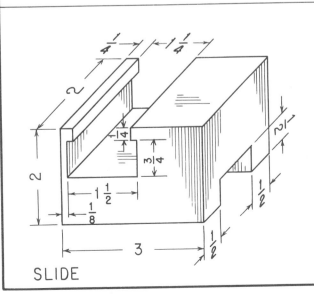

SLIDE

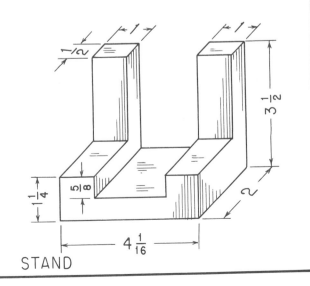

STAND

NON-ISOMETRIC LINES

The purpose of this unit is to teach the student to draw non-isometric lines, which are oblique to the isometric axes, and which do not appear in their true lengths on an isometric drawing.

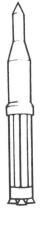

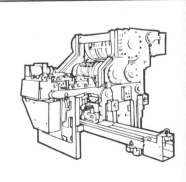

INFORMATION

In an isometric drawing, the lines that are oblique to the isometric axes are called non-isometric lines. Since a line of this type does not appear in its true length and cannot be measured directly, its position and projected length must be found by locating its end points.

PROBLEM

To make an isometric drawing of a block and include non-isometric lines.

INSTRUCTIONS

1. Draw border and title block.

2. In the center, draw the block with a slanting top shown on the following page.

3. Follow the step-by-step procedure for drawing non-isometric lines of the block.

4. Repeat in a similar manner for drawing non-isometric lines of other objects.

Isometric Drawing with Non-isometric Lines—1

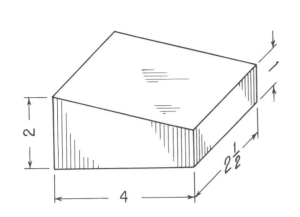

BLOCK WITH SLANTING TOP

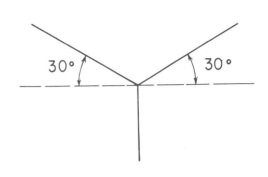

1. Draw the Isometric axes.

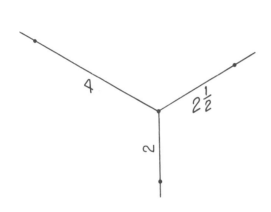

2. Measure off three dimensions 4″, 2″ and 2½″.

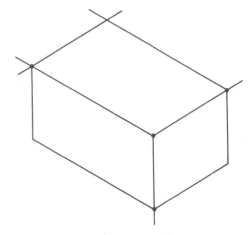

3. Draw the box in with light lines.

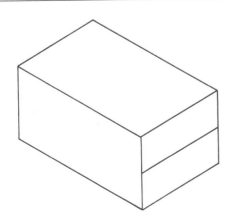

4. Locate the height of the slanting top on the front and rear faces.

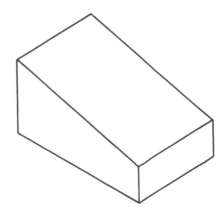

5. To draw the non-isometric lines, connect the points on the slanting top face as shown. Darken the object lines. Erase unwanted lines.

PROBLEM

Make isometric drawings of the objects shown in the group on the following page.

INSTRUCTIONS

1. Draw border lines and title block.

2. Divide the first sheet into two equal parts. In the first part, draw the pyramid and in the second part, draw the block.

3. Divide the second sheet into two equal parts. In the first part, draw the H-block and in the second part, draw the L-block.

4. Divide the third sheet into two equal parts. In the first part, draw the siding and in the second part, draw the base.

Note: Non-isometric lines are made by locating points on the rectangles they touch and connecting the points.

Isometric Drawing with Non-isometric Lines—2

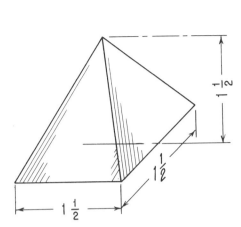

PYRAMID

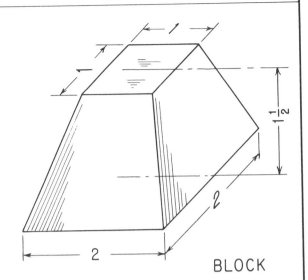

BLOCK

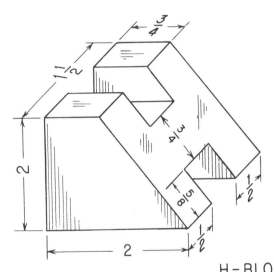

H—BLOCK

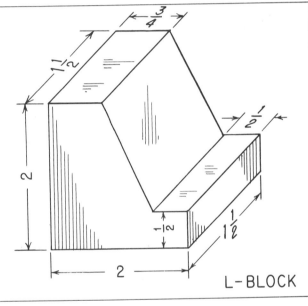

L—BLOCK

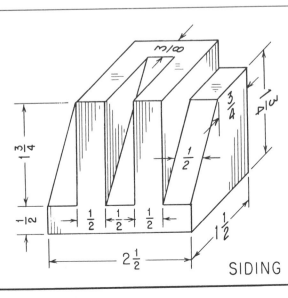

SIDING

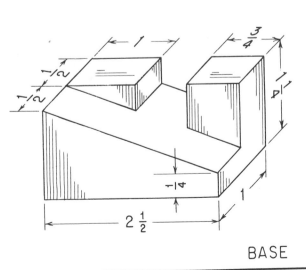

BASE

Units 5 and 6 review questions to be answered on a separate sheet of paper.

DIRECTIONS:

For each of the numbered statements below, write the number and after it the figure, symbol, word or words which will complete the sentence. Do NOT write in the book.

1. In an isometric drawing horizontal lines are drawn at _____ degrees with the horizontal.
   a) 30
   b) 60
   c) 90
   d) 45
   e) 180

2. The receding lines in an isometric drawing are _____.
   a) tangent
   b) parallel
   c) perpendicular
   d) equal
   e) slanted

3. An isometric drawing is a _____ drawing.
   a) perspective
   b) pictorial
   c) pencil
   d) colored
   e) working

4. In an isometric projection, vertical lines on the object appear _____ in the drawing.
   a) slanted
   b) perpendicular
   c) vertical
   d) rounded
   e) tangent

5. The three angles of an isometric axes are each _____ degrees.
   a) 60
   b) 30
   c) 90
   d) 180
   e) 120

6. An isometric drawing is a _____ view pictorial drawing.

7. All lines in an isometric drawing are drawn _____ to the axes.

8. An isometric "Y" is composed of three _____ degree angles.

9. In an isometric drawing, hidden lines are _____ unless necessary.

10. Isometric means _____ measure.

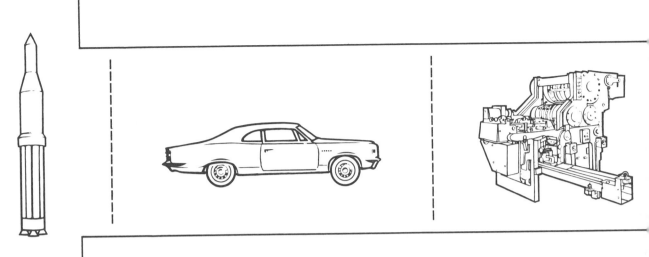

UNIT 7

ORTHOGRAPHIC PROJECTION

The purpose of this unit is to explain the meaning, character, and use of orthographic projection in mechanical drawing.

We have studied how to make pictorial drawings in oblique and isometric projection. Now we are to learn how to make a true view drawing in orthographic projection.

When we have to make the drawing of a machine with many parts, or a single machine part which is very complicated, a pictorial drawing is not enough. It does not describe the rear of an object, and it cannot describe what details exist inside the object. We therefore make a true view drawing which contains as many views as we need to describe the object, and we show each face as though we were looking at it squarely.

INFORMATION

Orthographic projection may be understood by considering the object to be drawn as placed in a transparent box hinged at the edges. The projections on the sides of the box are the views seen by looking straight at the object through each side. If the outlines were scribed on each surface and the box opened and laid flat as shown on the next page, the result would be a three-view orthographic projection drawing.

PROBLEM

Draw the three views that would appear in an orthographic projection drawing of a steel block 5 inches long, 1 inch high and 3 inches wide. Make the drawing full size.

INSTRUCTIONS

1. Draw border lines and title block.

2. Draw top, front and side views as shown at bottom of next page.

3. Be careful to line up the sides of top and front views and the top and bottom of front and side views.

4. Place dimensions on front and side views as shown.

Projecting the Three Orthographic Views

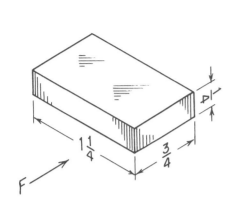

STEEL BLOCK

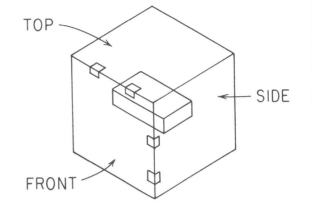

2. Place block in a hinged glass box.

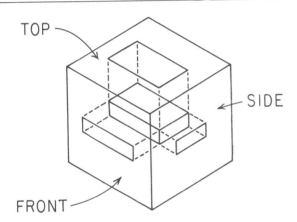

3. The views of the block are projected to the front, top and right sides of the glass box. (Planes of projection)

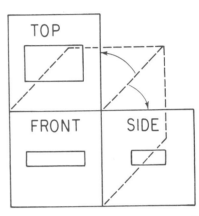

4. Fold the top and right-side planes in line with the front plane.

TOP

FRONT   SIDE

The result is an orthographic drawing.

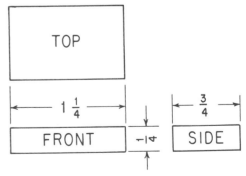

When the required dimensions are added, this becomes a working drawing.

INFORMATION

Orthographic projection is the method of representing the shape of an object in two or more views on planes at right angles to each other by extending perpendicular projection lines from the object to these planes.

Miter Line. A "mitre line" or line drawn at 45 degrees with the horizontal provides a ready means of "projecting" the end view from the front and top views or the top view from the front and end views.

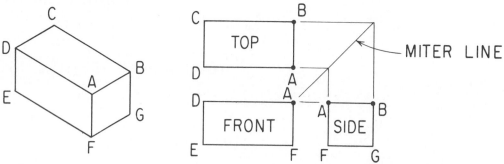

Thus, by means of this line, point A in the top view may be located in the end view by drawing a projection line horizontally to the right from this point until it meets the 45 degree mitre line and then vertically downward until it meets a projection line drawn horizontally from the same point A in the front view. The intersection of these two projection lines determines the position of point A in the side or end view. Point B in the end view is found in the same way except the horizontal projection from the front view is drawn from point A, since point B in this view lies directly behind point A and cannot be seen.

PROBLEM

Make a three-view orthographic projection drawing of the steel block shown in the isometric view on the following page.

INSTRUCTIONS

1. Draw border lines and title block.

2. Divide paper into two equal parts with a vertical line.

3. In the left-hand part draw the orthographic projection of the steel block.

4. Follow the step-by-step procedure carefully so that you will learn how to draw correctly a three-view orthographic projection.

5. Use a 4H pencil for construction lines and a 2H pencil for object lines.

Making an Orthographic Projection Drawing—1

STEEL BLOCK

FRONT

1. Select front face (the view that tells us most about the shape of the object).
2. Draw front face at lower left.

3. Extent projection lines upward representing width of front view.
4. Extend lines to the right representing the height of the view.

45°

5. Draw miter line at 45 degrees from upper right corner of front view.

6. Locate the top and side views.
7. Leave 1 inch between all views.

8. Darken object lines to complete the drawing.

INFORMATION

Ortho means "straight or at right angles" and *graphic* means "written or drawn." *Projection* comes from two old Latin words, "pro" meaning "forward" and "jacere" meaning "to throw." Thus *orthographic projection* literally means "thrown forward, drawn at right angles." The following definition has been given: Orthographic projection is the method of representing the exact form of an object in two or more views on planes generally at right angles to each other, by dropping perpendiculars from the object to the planes.

PROBLEM

Draw an orthographic drawing of the step block from the isometric drawing on the next page.

INSTRUCTIONS

1. Draw border lines and title block.

2. Use the step-by-step method shown on the next page to make the orthographic projection drawing.

Making an Orthographic Projection Drawing—2

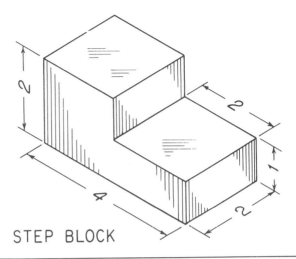

STEP BLOCK

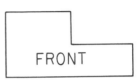

FRONT

1. Select as the front face the view that tells us most about the shape of the object.
2. Draw front face at lower left.

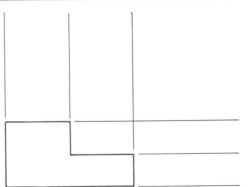

3. Extend projection lines upward representing width of front view.
4. Extend lines to the right representing the height of the view.

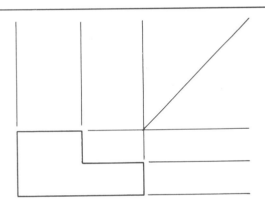

5. Draw miter line at 45 degrees from upper right corner of front view.

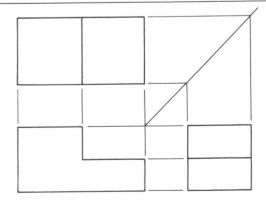

6. Locate the top and side views.
7. Leave 1 inch between all views and add details in the rectangular shape.

8. Darken object lines to complete drawing.

INFORMATION

In order for a draftsman to include the entire rendering of an object, it is essential for the object to be centered on the sheet of paper. To begin an orthographic projection drawing off center, means that one of the views may go off the paper.

PROBLEM

Show by calculations and diagrammatic sketch how to center an orthographic projection drawing within a given area for a given object such as the block shown below.

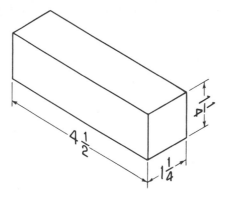

INSTRUCTIONS

1. Draw border lines and title block. Follow the step-by-step centering method in order to properly render three views of the block.

2. Determine the starting point of the drawing.

3. Enough room must be left for dimensions and notes.

4. Every drawing should be well-centered.

Finding Border Dimensions for Centering Drawing

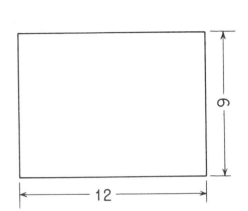

1. Draw a rectangle and mark it 9 X 12.

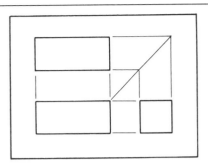

2. On the inside of this rectangle draw another rectangle of any convenient size.
3. At the corners of the smaller rectangle draw the outline of three views, as shown. (These do not need to be drawn exactly to scale.)

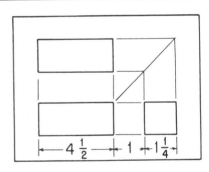

4. Mark in the length of the front view and the space between front and side views; also the width of the side view.

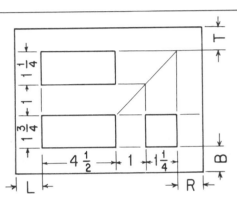

5. Mark in the height of the front view and the space between front and top views; also the width of the top view.

6. To find border widths L and R

Add: length of front view 4½
      length of space between
        front and side views 1
      width of side view 1¼
                        Sum 6-3/4

Subtract the sum from 12:   12
                                 − 6-3/4
                                   5¼

Divide this difference by 2:
              5¼ ÷ 2 = 2-5/8

Answer: The result is the width of spaces L and R for proper horizontal centering of the drawing.

7. To find border heights T and B

Add: height of front view 1¾
      height of space between
        front and top views 1
      height of top view 1¼
                        Sum 4

Subtract the sum from 9:   9
                                 −4
                                  5

Divide this difference by 2:
              5 ÷ 2 = 2½

Answer: The result is the height of spaces T and B for proper vertical centering of the drawing.

INFORMATION

A series of straight line problems provides the beginning student in Mechanical Drawing with experience which will develop skill in the application of the fundamental rules of orthographic projection.

The drawings in this unit are to be changed from isometric or picture drawings to orthographic or working drawings. The working drawing shows all lines in their true relative lengths. It is easily dimensioned and is the type most commonly used in industry. The views usually shown are the top, front, and right side. Notice the arrangement of the views as to position on the plate. This arrangement is the usual plan of all three-view drawings.

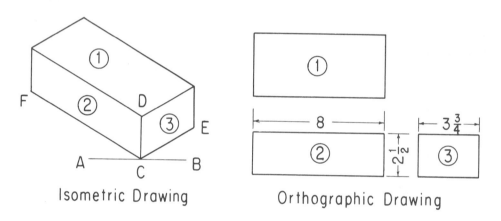

Isometric Drawing   Orthographic Drawing

PROBLEM

Change an isometric drawing of the brace shown on the next page to an orthographic projection drawing.

INSTRUCTIONS

1. Draw border lines and title block.

2. Draw light horizontal and vertical layout lines locating all three views of drawing.

3. Draw with instruments the top, front, and side views.

4. Show all hidden lines.

5. Omit dimensions.

6. Use a sharp 2H pencil and make all lines clean and dark so that a good print can be made from your drawing.

Practice in Orthographic Projection Drawing--1

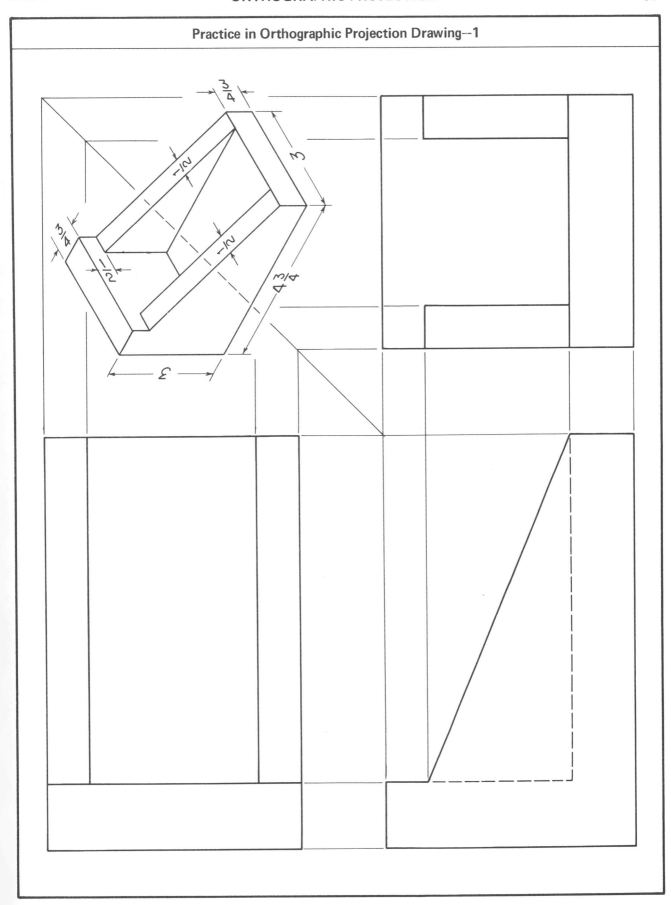

PROBLEM

To change an isometric projection drawing of the guide block shown on the next page to an orthographic projection drawing.

INSTRUCTIONS

1. Draw border lines and title block.

2. Draw light horizontal and vertical layout lines locating all three views of the drawing.

3. Draw with instruments the top, front, and side views.

4. Show all hidden lines.

5. Use a sharp 2H pencil for object lines.

Practice in Orthographic Projection Drawing—2

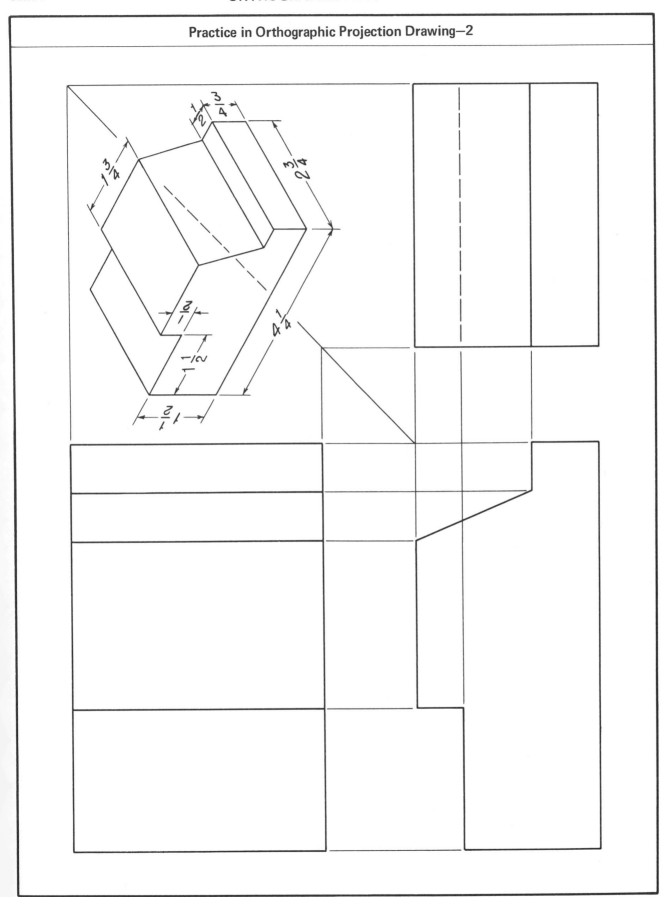

INFORMATION

A picture or photograph of an object would show it as it appears to the observer; however, it would not show the exact size, shape, and location of the various parts of the object.

To a mechanic, the working drawing is an instrument which gives him the instructions necessary for making the object shown. For this reason, a number of views are necessary, each showing that part of the object as it may appear to be seen by looking directly at one of the sides. Each view provides some of the information needed. The combination of views provides the total information needed for the complete object.

PROBLEM

Make a three-view drawing of each of the objects shown on the following page.

INSTRUCTIONS

1. Draw border lines and title block.

2. Use a miter line for correct projection.

3. Use a different sheet of paper for each job.

4. Omit dimensions.

Practice in Orthographic Projection Drawing—3

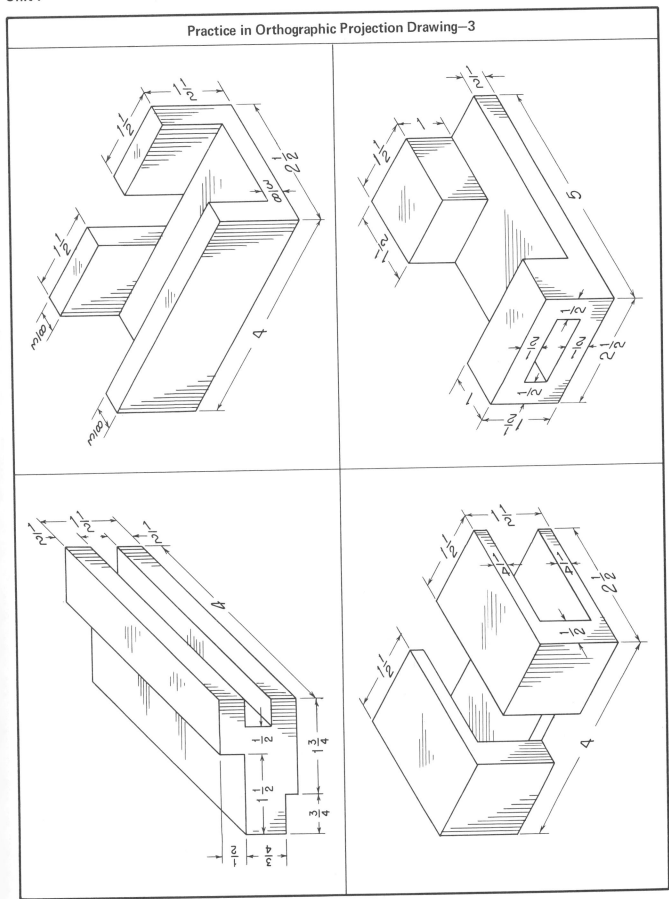

PROBLEM

Draw true view drawings of objects from the oblique and isometric projection drawings shown on the following page.

INSTRUCTIONS

1. Draw border lines and title block.

2. Make a true three-view drawing of the six drawings in this group.

3. Use a different sheet for each job.

4. Do not dimension.

5. Use a miter line for each construction.

Practice in Orthographic Projection Drawing—4

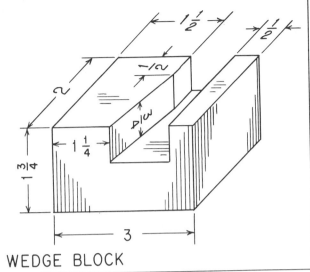

WEDGE BLOCK

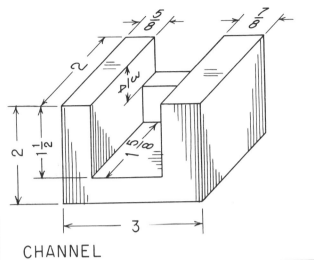

CHANNEL

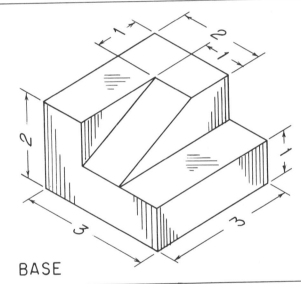

BASE

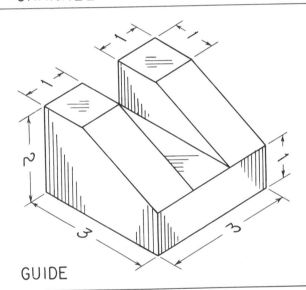

GUIDE

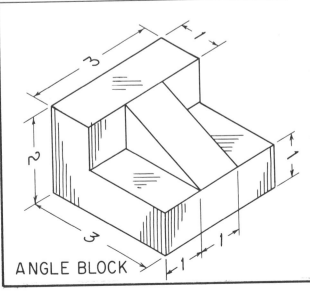

ANGLE BLOCK

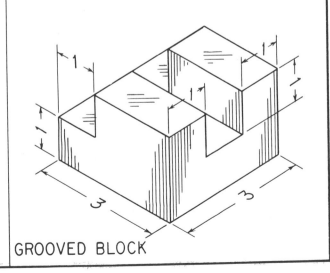

GROOVED BLOCK

Review Questions

Unit 7 review questions to be answered on a separate sheet of paper.

DIRECTIONS:

For each of the numbered statements below, write the number and after it the figure, symbol, word or words which will complete the sentence. Do NOT write in the book.

1. The angle of a miter line is _____ degrees.
   a) 30
   b) 60
   c) 45
   d) 90
   e) 180

2. The relationship between the side view and the front view is _____ degrees.
   a) 30
   b) 60
   c) 90
   d) 120
   e) 45

3. The views that show the width of an object are _____.
   a) front and top
   b) top and side
   c) front and bottom
   d) bottom and top
   e) left side and front

4. The normal planes of projection for an object are _____.
   a) 2
   b) 4
   c) 6
   d) 3
   e) 5

5. The three views commonly shown on a drawing are top, front and _____ side.
   a) bottom
   b) left
   c) right
   d) top
   e) front

Review Questions (continued)

6. In orthographic projection, the right side view is placed to the right of and facing the _____.
   a) front view
   b) top view
   c) bottom view
   d) rear view
   e) left side

7. The top view is always _____.
   a) below front view
   b) above front view
   c) to the right of front view
   d) to the left of front view
   e) on bottom

8. The length of the front view is the same in _____.
   a) top view
   b) right side view
   c) left side view
   d) bottom view
   e) oblique

9. A drawing in orthographic projection has _____, usually.
   a) two views
   b) three views
   c) one view
   d) as many as needed
   e) four views

10. A drawing in orthographic projection shows all lines in _____.
    a) angles
    b) oblique
    c) slant
    d) true lengths
    e) isometric

Review Problem: Below are two of the usual three orthographic views of four different objects. Draw the missing view of each.

LINES AND DIMENSIONS

The purpose of this unit is to show how to correctly use the standard lines, symbols, figures and notes in making working drawings.

If a drawing is to serve its intended use, it must not only show the shape of the objects, but in addition, it must contain information as to sizes of the pieces, kinds of material to be used, the number of parts required, and such other essential data as may be needed to construct the object. In addition, the drawing must furnish the workman with information on the distance between surfaces, location of holes, kind of finish, type of material, number required, etc. The expression of this information on a drawing by the use of lines, symbols, figures and notes is known as dimensioning. In this unit you will learn about basic dimensioning.

INFORMATION

Heavy lines: The main outline of the object is usually the most important part of a working drawing. The visible edge, or object line, should be a heavy solid line made with an F lead and a strong stroke. What is known as a section line is also drawn as a heavy line.

Medium lines: The hidden part of the object outline in any given view is shown by a medium dashed line. This should be drawn with a 2H lead.

Light lines: All the other lines used to complete the drawing are to be made thin so as not to detract from the effect of the main outline. In this category are such lines as:

a. extension — drawn as solid light lines
b. dimension — drawn as solid light lines
c. center — drawn as dot-and-dash light lines
d. section — drawn as solid light lines

These should be drawn with a 2H lead.

Arrow heads: Note the proportions of the arrow heads used at the ends of dimension lines. Neat, well-proportioned arrow heads add greatly to the appearance of a mechanical drawing.

PROBLEM

To become familiar with various kinds of drafting lines and where they are used.

INSTRUCTIONS

Copy the Alphabet of Lines in your graph paper notebook. Make all letters 1/8 inch high.

The Alphabet of Lines

The symbols used by the draftsman in his drawings are a combination of drafting abbreviations, lines, and figures. It can also be called "Pictorial Writing".

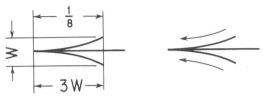

ARROW HEADS

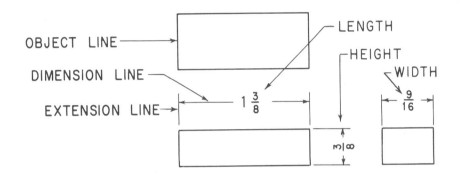

Outline of Parts	————————— HEAVY —————————	The outline should be the outstanding feature and the thickness may vary to suit size of drawing.
Section Lines	————————— LIGHT —————————	Space evenly to make a shaded effect.
Hidden Lines	– – – – – MEDIUM – – – – –	Short dashes.
Center Lines	—— - —— LIGHT —— - ——	Broken line, made up of long and short dashes, alternately spaced.
Dimension and Extension Lines	LIGHT |←——— 3 ½ ———→|	Lines unbroken, except at dimensions.
Cutting Plane Line	—— – – —— HEAVY —— – – ——	Broken line line made up of one long and two short dashes, alternately spaced.

PROBLEM

In your graph notebook, copy definitions of lines for dimensioning from the following page.

INSTRUCTIONS

Use 1/8-inch high vertical, capital letters for definitions in your graph notebook.

How Different Lines Are Used

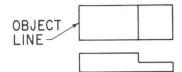

The object lines should be the outstanding feature. Their thickness may vary to suit the size of drawing. They are usually heavy lines.

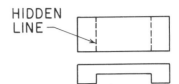

The hidden lines represent edges that are hidden from view and which must be shown. They are usually medium lines.

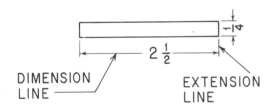

Extension lines are the short lines that show to which part of the object the dimension refers. They lead from a point about 1/16 inch from the object and extend about 1/16 inch beyond the arrowhead.

Dimension lines show the distance to which the dimension refers. They are drawn 1/4 inch away from the object lines.

Both extension and dimension are usually light lines.

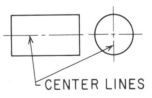

Center lines locate the centers of circles and the axes of symmetrical objects. They are usually light lines.

INFORMATION

Dashed lines are used on an external view of an object to represent surfaces and intersections invisible at the point from which the view is taken.

PROBLEM

Illustrate the technique of drawing hidden lines.

INSTRUCTIONS

Draw and label the four types of hidden line intersections shown on the following page. Use your graph notebook.

Also draw in your graph notebook the three orthographic views of the channel shown at the top of that page.

How Hidden Lines are Shown

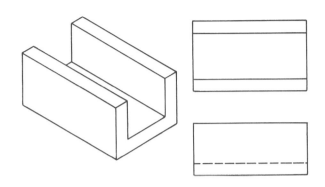

HIDDEN
EDGES WHEN
VIEWED
FROM THE
FRONT

There are hidden edges in objects which cannot be seen from the outside of the piece. These hidden edges are also called invisible edges. They are represented by a series of small dash---- lines known as hidden lines.

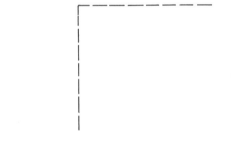

1. Hidden lines meeting at a corner have two dashes meeting at the corner.

2. A hidden line intersects a visible line with a dash in contact.

3. A hidden line intersects another hidden line at the crossing point of two dashes in contact.

4. Three hidden lines meeting at a corner have three dashes intersecting at the corner.

Review Questions

Unit 8 review questions to be answered on a separate sheet of paper.

DIRECTIONS:
For each of the numbered statements below, write the number and after it the figure, symbol, word or words which will complete the sentence. Do NOT write in the book.

1. An outline of a part is a _____ line.
   a) medium
   b) dash
   c) heavy
   d) light
   e) broken

2. A hidden line is a _____ line.
   a) medium
   b) light
   c) heavy
   d) broken
   e) dimension

3. A dimension line is a _____ line.
   a) light
   b) broken
   c) heavy
   d) medium
   e) length

4. Short dashes are found in _____ lines.
   a) extension
   b) dimension
   c) object
   d) width
   e) hidden

5. A broken line, made up of long and short dashes, alternately spaced is a/an _____ line.
   a) section
   b) cutting plane
   c) center
   d) extension
   e) length

6. Dimension lines should be placed about _____ inch from the views.
   a) 1/8
   b) 1/16
   c) 1/2
   d) 1/4
   e) 3/8

7. Extension lines are _____ unbroken lines.
   a) heavy
   b) medium
   c) light
   d) sloping
   e) oblique

8. Arrowheads are placed on the _____ of the dimension lines.
   a) middle
   b) ends
   c) half
   d) inside
   e) bottom

9. Visible edge lines are _____ lines.
   a) very light
   b) heavy
   c) light
   d) medium
   e) thin

10. Hidden edges are called _____ edges.
    a) invisible
    b) oblique
    c) phantom
    d) solid
    e) dark

INFORMATION

The principles of orthographic projection are:

1. The front and side views are in line horizontally.

2. The front and top views are in line vertically.

3. The front of the object in the top view faces the front view.

4. The depth of the top view is the same as the depth of the side.

5. The length of the top is the same as the length of the front view.

PROBLEM

Make orthographic drawings from objects shown.

INSTRUCTIONS

1. Divide two sheets of paper each into two parts.

2. On the first sheet make an orthographic projection drawing of the Channel and of the Grooved Block.

3. Show all three views in each drawing.

4. On the second sheet make an orthographic projection drawing of the Bevel Block and of the Slide.

5. Show all three views in each drawing.

6. Refer to page 109 for examples of the proper way to draw invisible lines.

7. Do not dimension.

Line Practice in Orthographic Projection Drawing

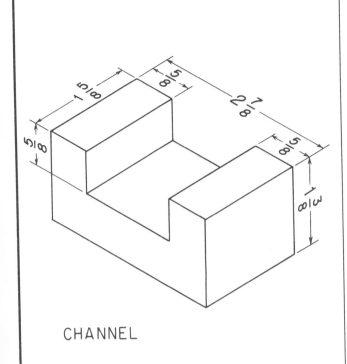

CHANNEL

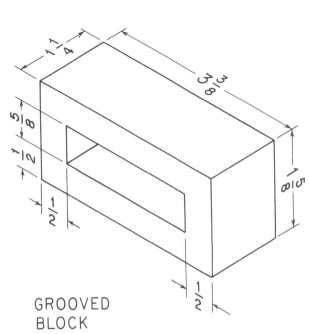

GROOVED
BLOCK

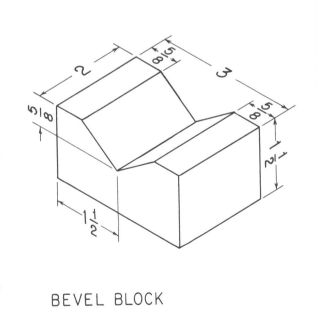

BEVEL BLOCK

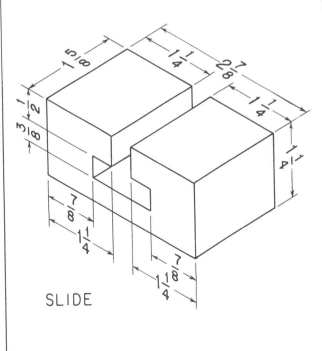

SLIDE

PROBLEM

Dimension the rectangular shapes shown on the following page.

INSTRUCTIONS

1. Draw border lines and title block.

2. Divide sheet into six equal spaces.

3. In each space make an orthographic projection drawing of each figure shown.

   a. First draw the proper number of views of the subject.

   b. Second, study the views as though you were the workman and see what dimensions you would need to make the object.

   c. Third, plan the location of these dimensions for convenience in use, bearing in mind the rules that you have learned.

Practice in Dimensioning—Rectangular Shapes

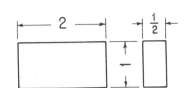

1. Dimension lines should be aligned when possible

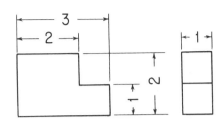

2. Place any smaller dimensions nearer to the view than the larger dimensions along the same side or edge.

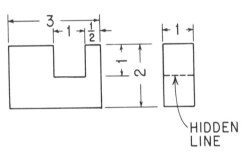

3. Place dimensions between views (when practical).

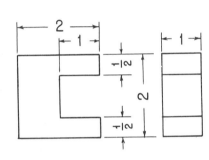

4. Dimensions should be placed so that they will read from the bottom and from the right.

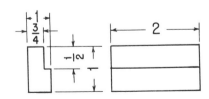

5. Dimension to a profile face whenever possible.

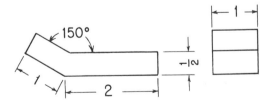

6. Angles are dimensioned with two arrows in the form of an arc.

INFORMATION

In a mechanical drawing the orthographic projections will clearly define the shape of the object. Before the drawing can be used, however, it must include all necessary dimensions for the sizes of all parts and their relationships with one another. Notes may also be needed to give other information needed for construction.

PROBLEM

Draw and dimension the figures shown on the following page. Note that each requires the dimensioning of circular elements for size and location.

INSTRUCTIONS

1. Draw border lines and title block.

2. Divide sheet into six equal spaces.

3. In each space make an orthographic projection drawing of the figure shown.

   a. First draw the proper number of views of the subject.

   b. Second, study the views as though you were the workman and see what dimensions you would need to make the object.

   c. Third, plan the location of these dimensions for convenience in use, bearing in mind the rules that you have learned.

Practice in Dimensioning—Circular Shapes

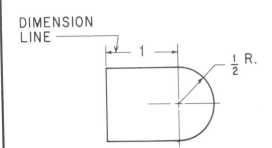

1. An arc is dimensioned by indicating the radius.

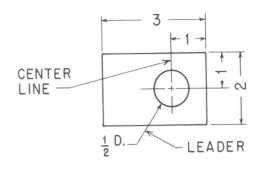

2. The size of a circle is indicated by giving the diameter.

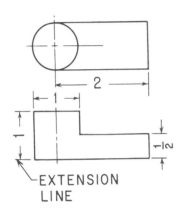

3. Dimension the profile view of a cylinder.

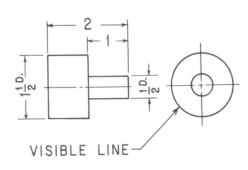

4. Give overall lengths of cylinders.

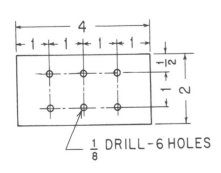

5. Dimension similar circles by means of a note.

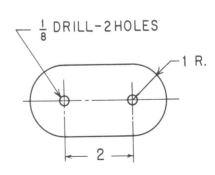

6. Locate the hole centers, do not give overall length of the part.

INFORMATION

1. Dimensions on a drawing should be read from left to right horizontally. This corresponds to the way we read all printed matter.

2. Some dimensions, however, are in a vertical direction and so cannot be arranged as in rule 1. These dimensions should read from the bottom toward the top. In other words, it should be possible to read every dimension on a drawing from either the bottom or right side.

3. Diameters and radii of arcs and circles are an exception to this rule, since they must never be placed along center lines. They should, however, be placed at as small an angle with the horizontal and vertical as possible.

PROBLEM

Make two-view drawings of the objects shown on the following page. Add necessary dimensions.

INSTRUCTIONS

1. Draw border lines and title block.

2. Divide paper into four equal parts.

3. Measure objects for dimensions.

4. Draw two views and dimension fully all four objects.

Further Practice in Dimensioning—1

STOP

BASE

ANGLE

SUPPORT

Further Practice in Dimensioning—2

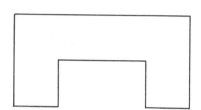

1. The length of this object is 2 inches. The slot is 1 inch long. Dimension both lengths.

2. Dimension this object. Length of A = 1-3/4". Length of B = 1".

3. Dimension this view, which is 1-1/2" X 3/4".

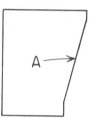

4. The length of Line A is 7/8 inch. Show how you would dimension line A.

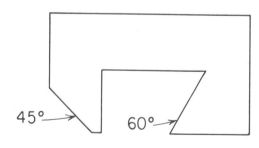

5. Dimension both angles.

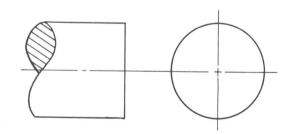

6. The diameter equals 1 inch. Dimension profile view.

Further Practice in Dimensioning—3

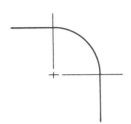

7. The radius of this curve is 1/2 inch. Show dimension.

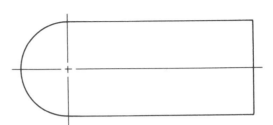

8. This object is drawn full scale. Dimension the length. (Use ruler.)

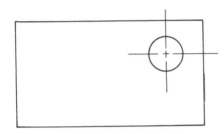

9. The hole in this plate is made with a 3/8-inch drill. How would you show this on a drawing?

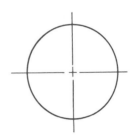

10. This circle has a diameter of 1 inch. Dimension it as you would on a drawing.

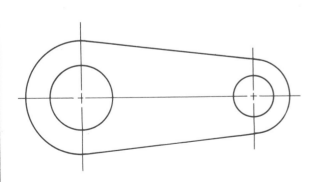

11. Measure center-to-center distance and show the dimension.

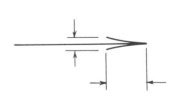

12. Give dimensions for arrowhead proportions.

Review Questions

Unit 8 review questions to be answered on a separate sheet of paper.

DIRECTIONS

For each of the numbered statements below, write the number and after it the figure, symbol, word or words which will complete the sentence. Do NOT write in the book.

1. Use _____ lead pencil for dimensioning.
    a) H
    b) F
    c) 2H
    d) 3H
    e) 4H

2. Dimensions should read from the bottom and _____ side.
    a) left
    b) bottom
    c) right
    d) vertical
    e) parallel

3. Place dimensions _____ views on a drawing.
    a) front
    b) side
    c) between
    d) slanted
    e) on

4. Dimension a circle by giving its _____.
    a) circumference
    b) diameter
    c) radius
    d) volume
    e) edge

5. Dimension an arc by giving its _____.
    a) angle
    b) diameter
    c) surface
    d) center line
    e) radius

Review Questions (continued)

6. Dimensions usually appear on _____ drawings.
   a) isometric
   b) oblique
   c) working
   d) perspective
   e) orthographic

7. Similar holes are dimensioned by means of a _____.
   a) radius
   b) blank
   c) note
   d) letters
   e) numbers

8. The bar dividing a fraction should be _____ to the bottom of the dimension.
   a) diagonal
   b) scaled
   c) parallel
   d) slanted
   e) angular

9. Place small dimensions _____ to the view.
   a) slanted
   b) oblique
   c) nearer
   d) further
   e) revolved

10. Leaders are usually drawn at an angle of _____ degrees.
    a) 45
    b) 15
    c) 75
    d) 60
    e) 90

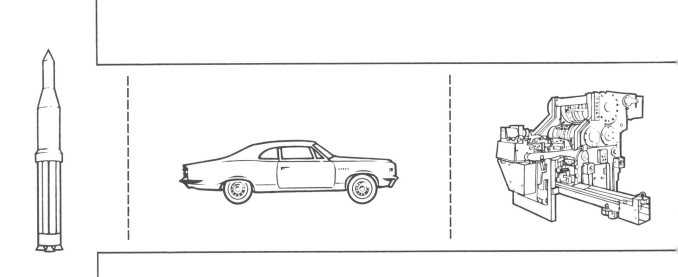

UNIT 9

SCALE DRAWING

The purpose of this unit is to teach drawing to scale.

We know that when an object is too large to be drawn to its full size, it is necessary to draw it smaller and to proportion. For example, to draw to full size the plans of an engine would require a piece of paper much too large to draw upon. When an object is very small, it is drawn larger than full size. The architects scale is made for drawing to scale and it is so marked that you will have little difficulty in making drawings smaller or larger than full size. The dimension numbers on the drawing give the actual size measurement of the object. The numbers never change regardless of the scale to which the drawing is made.

INFORMATION

This is an introductory lesson to the use of a scale in drafting.

Scales

A drawing of an object is a "full size" drawing if it is the same size as the object itself. A normal scale is used such as that shown below. Quite frequently, however, the draftsman must make a drawing of a large object which may extend up to several hundred feet. In order to produce such a drawing, it is necessary to make it smaller than the object, or "to scale." The most common scales used are the Architect's, the Civil Engineer's, and the Mechanical Engineer's. The Architect's Scale is used in mechanical drafting.

Reading the Normal Scale

The figure below shows the divisions of a normal scale. This looks the same as an ordinary ruler. The major unit of this scale represents one inch, and it is divided into sixteen subdivisions, each representing one-sixteenth of an inch.

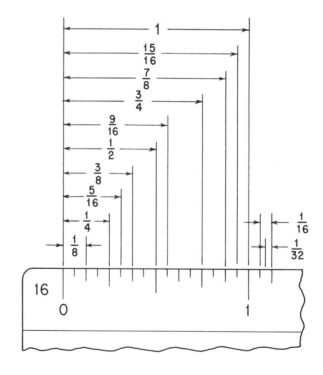

INFORMATION

This is a demonstration of how a simple scale drawing is made.

When the draftsman makes drawings of a large machine, does he use a sheet as long as the machine—or as high?

Obviously, he must reduce the size of his drawing. *For example:* If a machine is 3 feet high, the draftsman will have to scale down the machine so that it will fit on the sheet. If the drawing is to be of a small object, such as a bolt, he will want to enlarge it.

A *scale* is used to indicate the ratio of the size of the view or views as drawn to the actual size of the object.

Full size is the scale which will be used wherever practicable.

An *enlarged scale* may be used when the actual size of the object is so small that a full size drawing would not present clearly the features of the object.

A *reduced scale* may be used when the actual size of the object is so large that a full scale drawing would exceed the available paper space. However, reduction should be limited to that scale which will provide the necessary clarity.

Shown below are three drawings of a 1-inch square drawn to: (A) half size, (B) full size and (C) twice size.

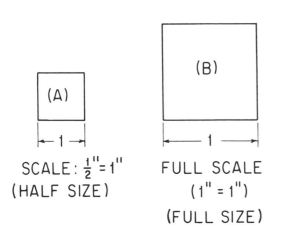

SCALE: $\frac{1}{2}$" = 1"
(HALF SIZE)

FULL SCALE
(1" = 1")
(FULL SIZE)

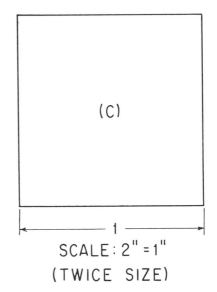

SCALE: 2" = 1"
(TWICE SIZE)

INFORMATION

This is an explanation of what an architect's scale is and how it is used. The architect's scale is usually constructed of thoroughly seasoned boxwood with divisions indicated along both sides of each edge. It may be flat, somewhat similar to an ordinary ruler, except that scales are on both edges and both sides of each edge, or it may be triangular with scales on each side of three edges as shown on the following page.

Each major division represents one foot and every other one is numbered, 2, 4, 6, 8, etc. These major divisions are on one side of the zero line. On the other side of the zero line (see individual scale illustrations on the following page) are twelve smaller divisions, each representing one inch. There are eleven different scales on an architect's triangular rule, as explained on the following page.

PROBLEM

To become familiar with the architect's scale and to use it for a simple scale drawing.

INSTRUCTIONS

Carefully study the different scales on an architect's rule as explained on the following page. Then draw four 1'4''-squares to the following scales: one-half size, one-quarter size, one-eighth size, and one-sixteenth size.

1. Draw borderlines and title block.

2. Carefully center the half-size square within the border.

3. Draw each of the other three reduced-size squares, also centered on the paper. Thus, each will be within the next larger square.

4. Dimension one side of each square.

5. Label each square as ONE-HALF SIZE, ONE-QUARTER SIZE, ONE-EIGHTH SIZE, and ONE-SIXTEENTH SIZE.

Using the Architects Scale

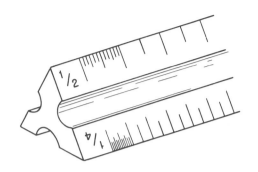

Architect's scale or rule

In order to simplify the making of scale drawings, the architect's rule was developed. One edge of the triangular rule is graduated as a standard 12 inch ruler, in units of 1/16 inch. The other edges are calibrated to standard scales that are commonly used in drafting.

Examination of this type of scale will show that it can be used for ten different common scales.

Architect's Scales

Scale Designation	Scale	Amount of Reduction
16	12 inches represents 1 foot	Full size
3	3 inches represents 1 foot	One-quarter size
1 1/2	1 1/2 inches represents 1 foot	One-eighth size
1	1 inch represents 1 foot	One-twelfth size
3/4	3/4 inch represents 1 foot	One-sixteenth size
1/2	1/2 inch represents 1 foot	One-twenty-fourth size
3/8	3/8 inch represents 1 foot	One-thirty-second size
1/4	1/4 inch represents 1 foot	One-forty-eighth size
3/16	3/16 inch represents 1 foot	One-sixty-fourth size
1/8	1/8 inch represents 1 foot	One-ninety-sixth size
3/32	3/32 inch represents 1 foot	One-one-hundred-twenty-eighth size

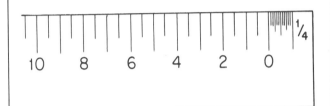

This shows the scale on the architect's rule marked 1/4. It is used to draw lines directly to 1/48 size. Notice that the smaller divisions representing inches are at the right of the zero mark and the larger ones representing feet are at the left. You use this scale from right to left.

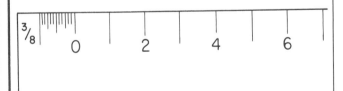

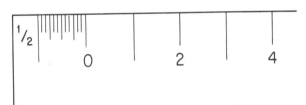

This shows the scale on the architect's rule marked 3/8. The one big division to the left of the zero point is the same length as each division to the right of the zero point. Like those to the right, it represents one foot. Since it is divided into 12 parts, each small part represents 1 inch.

This shows the scale on the architect's rule marked 1/2. This part is used to draw lines directly to 1/24 size. Suppose you want to represent a distance 2'4" long to 1/24 size. To do this, you draw a line from the 4-inch mark (four small spaces to the left of the zero mark) to the division marked 2 (two large spaces to the right of the zero mark).

INFORMATION

In the full-size scale each small division is 1/16 inch, as in an ordinary ruler. Note that each inch is divided first into halves, then quarters, then eighths, and finally six-teenths.

For half-size drawings use the full-size scale but divide every dimension mentally by two. To set off 1 inch, for example, measure 1/2 inch, etc. Do not use the 1/2 scale which is intended for drawings to a scale of 1/2" = 1'0".

For quarter-size drawings use the 3 scale in which 3" = 1'0". The subdivided portion to the right of zero represents 1'0" and is divided into inches, then half-inches, quarter-inches, and eighth-inches. The entire portion representing 1'0" would actually measure 3 inches; therefore, 3" = 1'0".

PROBLEM

Make a three-view drawing of each problem. Dimension and use reduced scale. Scale: half-size.

INSTRUCTIONS

1. Draw border lines and title block.
2. Make a three-view drawing of each problem.
3. Use a scale of 1/2 inch = 1 inch. This reduced scale is used because the actual dimensions of the objects are too large to fit on 8-1/2 x 11-inch paper.

Tips on Measuring

1. Keep the scale clean.
2. Eye the scale directly from above.
3. Use a sharp pencil.
4. Use the largest scale that will fit the paper.
5. Use scale only for measuring and *not for drawing lines.* Draw the line first to approximate length, then transfer the measurement directly from the scale when held against the line. Another method is to set a pair of dividers to the required length on the scale and transfer it to the proper line on the drawing with dividers.
6. Do not move the scale to take individual measurements when laying off a series of distances along a line.
7. Recheck measurements after laying them off.

Practice in Scale Drawing

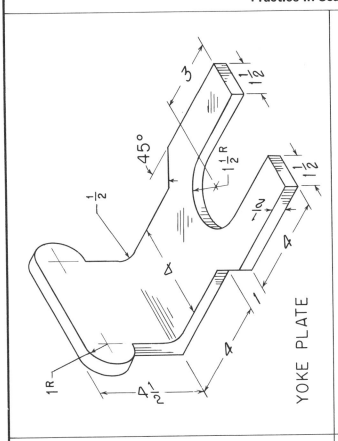

YOKE PLATE

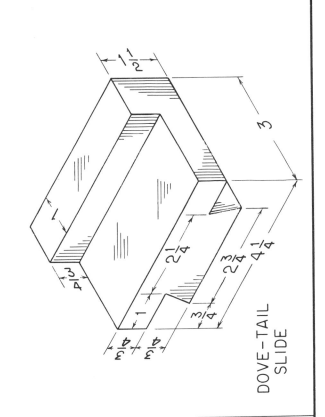

DOVE-TAIL SLIDE

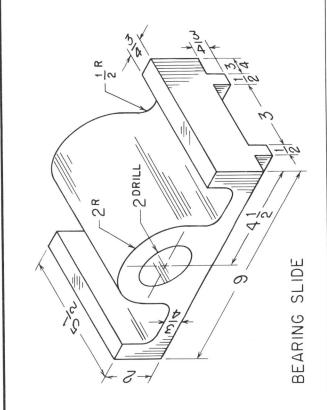

BEARING SLIDE

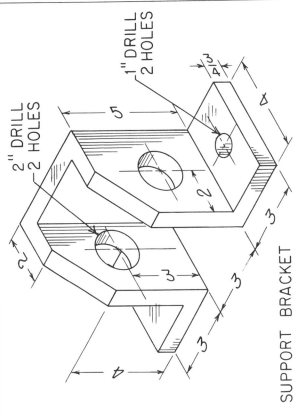

SUPPORT BRACKET

Review Questions

Unit 9 review questions to be answered on a separate sheet of paper.

DIRECTIONS

For each of the numbered statements below, write the number and after it the figure, symbol, word or words which will complete the sentence. Do NOT write in the book.

1. Full size means: 12 inches on drawing equals 12 inches on _____ .
   a) radius
   b) diameter
   c) object
   d) ruler
   e) scale

2. Inch marks are _____ used when all dimensions are in inches.
   a) not
   b) sometimes
   c) always
   d) lightly
   e) hardly

3. ¼ size means 3 inches on drawing equals _____ on object.
   a) 4"
   b) 8"
   c) 12"
   d) 16"
   e) 5"

4. The architect's scale has _____ different common scales.
   a) 2
   b) 4
   c) 6
   d) 8
   e) 10
   f) 11

5. The architect's scale is used for enlarging or _____ a drawing of an object.
   a) darkening
   b) reducing
   c) shading
   d) representing
   e) copying

Review Questions (continued)

6. The Architect's scale may be _____ or _____ in shape.
   a) octagonal
   b) triangular
   c) square
   d) flat
   e) round

7. Scale: 1" = 1" is the same as _____ size.
   a) quarter
   b) eighth
   c) full
   d) half
   e) three quarter

8. Scale: ½" = 1" is the same as _____ size.
   a) quarter
   b) eighth
   c) full
   d) half
   e) three quarter

9. ½ size means 3 inches on drawing equals _____ on object.
   a) 2"
   b) 4"
   c) 12"
   d) 6"
   e) 8"

10. Scale: ¼" = 1" is the same as _____ size.
    a) quarter
    b) eighth
    c) full
    d) half
    e) 1/48

DIMENSIONED DRAWINGS

The purpose of this unit is to provide practice in producing dimensioned drawings in orthographic projection.

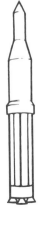

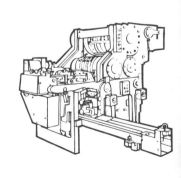

INFORMATION

A working drawing may be defined as a drawing containing an adequate number of views of an object, completely dimensioned, and having sufficient notes to enable one to make the object without further information.

PROBLEM

Make a working drawing of each of the objects shown on the following page.

INSTRUCTIONS

1. Draw border lines and title block.

2. Draw three views of each of the six objects shown.

3. Add necessary dimensions.

4. Use more than one sheet of paper if necessary.

Practice in Making Working Drawings

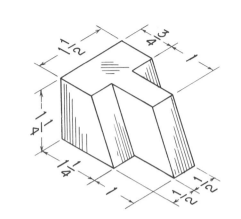

BASE

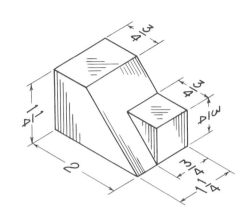

CORNER BLOCK

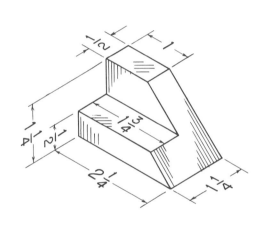

STAND

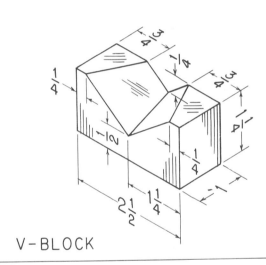

V–BLOCK

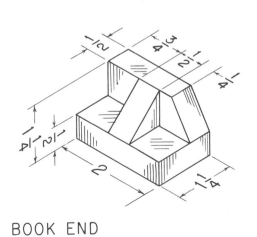

BOOK END

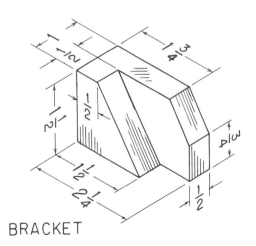

BRACKET

UNIT 11

CONSTRUCTING LINES AND ANGLES

The purpose of this unit is to show how certain lines and angles can be drawn by geometric construction.

These and the geometric constructions shown in Units 12 and 13 have important uses in making drawings and in solving problems using diagrams or graphs.

The mechanical drafting student should be able to make all of the more commonly used constructions.

INFORMATION

Using only a straightedge, such as a T-square, and a draftsman's compass, a line or an angle can be bisected, a line can be drawn through a given point and at right angles to a given line, or a given angle may be copied. This is done by means of what is called a geometric construction, that is a construction based on certain principles of geometry.

PROBLEM

Make the constructions shown on pages 141 and 142.

INSTRUCTIONS

1. Draw borderlines and title block.

2. Divide paper into six equal parts.

3. In each part make one of the constructions shown.

4. Follow each step carefully.

Construction No. 1: Bisect a given line.

	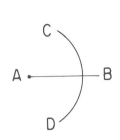	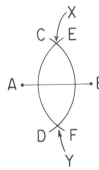	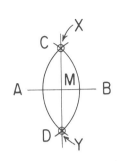
Given: Line A-B	1. With radius greater than half of A-B draw arc C-D with center at A.	2. With same radius draw arc E-F with center at B to locate X and Y.	3. Connect intersections X and Y to bisect line A-B at M.

Construction No. 2: Draw a perpendicular through a given point outside a given line.

Given: Line X-Y and point P.	1. Using point P as a center draw arc A-B.	2. Draw arc C-D with center at B.	3. Draw arc E-F with center at A and with same R to locate point G.	4. Connect P and G to erect perpendicular.

Construction No. 3: Draw a perpendicular through a given point within a given line.

	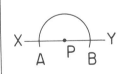		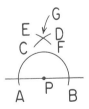	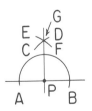
Given: Line X-Y and point P.	1. Draw semi-circle A-B with center at P.	2. Draw arc C-D with center at B.	3. Draw arc E-F with center at A and same radius as arc C-D to locate G.	4. Connect P and G to erect perpendicular.

Construction No. 4: Divide a given line into seven equal parts.

A ——————— B

Given: Line A-B

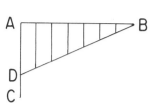

1. Draw A-C at right angles to A-B.

2. Select some convenient point D on A-C so that D-B can be easily divided into seven equal parts and mark these off.

3. From each point on D-B draw a line parallel to A-C and intersecting A-B. Line A-B will then be divided into seven equal parts.

Construction No. 5: Bisect a given angle.

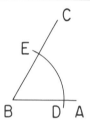

Given: Angle C-B-A

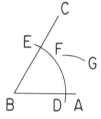

1. Draw arc E-D with center at B.

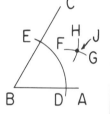

2. Draw arc F-G with center at D.

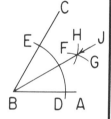

3. Draw arc H-I with center at E and with same radius as F-G to locate J.

4. Connect J and B to bisect given angle.

Construction No. 6: Copy a given angle.

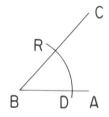

Given: Angle C-B-A Draw arc R-D of any convenient radius with B as a center.

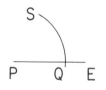

1. Draw P-E equal to B-A. Draw arc Q-S so that P-Q equals B-D.

2. Mark off with compass distance Q-T equal to D-R.

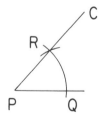

3. Draw P-R-C to complete angle.

CONSTRUCTING GEOMETRIC FIGURES

The purpose of this unit is to show how certain geometrical figures: triangles, squares, hexagons, octagons, stars, and ellipses, can be readily constructed with straight edge, compass, and occasionally with the aid of a draftsman's triangle.

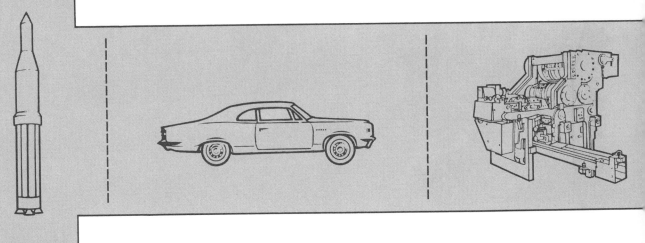

INFORMATION

Using only a straightedge and a compass it is possible to construct an equilateral (equal-sided) triangle, to construct a triangle having given an angle, a side and an angle, and to copy a triangle having three unequal sides.

PROBLEM

Construct the triangles shown on page 145.

INSTRUCTIONS

1. Draw borderlines and title block.

2. Divide the drawing space into three equal parts.

3. In each part construct one of the triangles shown on page 145.

4. Follow each step carefully.

Construction No. 7: Construct an equilateral triangle.

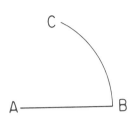

Given: Side A-B.

1. Draw arc B-C with center at A.

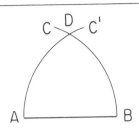

2. Draw arc A-C' with center at B.

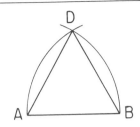

3. Draw sides A-D and B-D to complete triangle.

Construction No. 8: Construct a triangle, angle-side-angle.

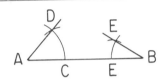

Given: Side A-B and angles at A and B.

1. Draw line A'-B' equal to A-B.

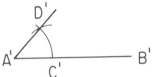

2. Draw arc C'-D' to copy angle at A as in Construction No. 6.

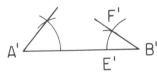

3. Draw arc E'-F' to copy angle at B.

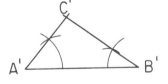

4. Continue sides of both angles until they intersect at C', completing triangle.

Construction No. 9: Copy a triangle with three unequal sides.

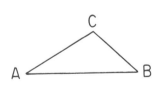

Given: Triangle A-B-C.

1. Draw line A'-B' equal to A-B.

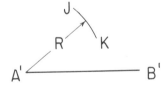

2. With R equal to given side A-C and A' as a center draw arc J-K.

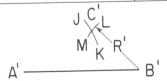

3. With R' equal to given side B-C and B' as a center, draw arc L-M to intersect arc J-K at C'.

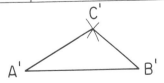

4. Draw A'-C' and B'-C' to complete triangle.

INFORMATION

1. If a diagonal of a square, a hexagon, or an octagon is given, it is possible to construct the figure on it using only a compass and a straightedge.

2. If one side of a hexagon is given, the entire figure can be drawn using only a compass and a straightedge.

PROBLEM

1. To construct a square, a hexagon and an octagon along a given diagonal.

2. To construct a hexagon on a given side.

INSTRUCTIONS

1. Draw borders and title block.

2. Divide paper into four equal parts.

3. Draw the given diagonal AB in the center of the first three spaces.

4. In the first space construct the square; in the second, the hexagon; and in the third, the octagon.

5. In the fourth space construct a hexagon on the given side.

6. Follow each step carefully.

Construction No. 10: Construct a square on a given diagonal.

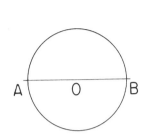

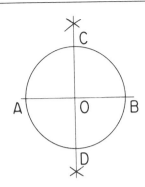

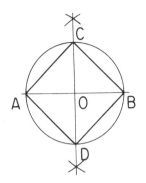

Given: Diagonal length A-B. Draw a circle of this diameter.

Construct a perpendicular bisector C-D.

Connect points A-C, C-B, B-D and D-A to complete the square.

Construction No. 11: Construct a hexagon on a given diagonal.

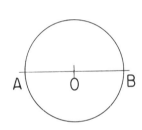

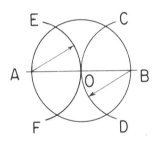

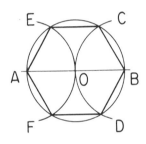

Given: Diagonal length A-B. Draw a circle of this diameter.

Draw arc C-D with B as a center and arc E-F with A as a center to locate C, D, E, and F.

Connect A-E, E-C, C-B, B-D, D-F and F-A to complete the hexagon.

Construction No. 12: Construct an octagon on a given diagonal.

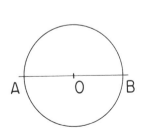

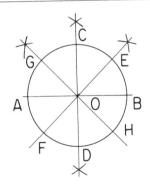

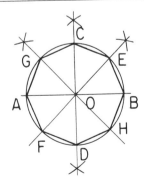

Given: Diagonal length A-B. Draw a circle of this diameter.

Draw the perpendicular bisector C-D. Bisect angle C-O-A to locate G and H. Bisect angle C-O-B to locate E and F.

Connect A-G, G-C, C-E, E-B, B-H, H-D, D-F and F-A to complete the octagon.

Construction No. 13: Construct a hexagon with one side given.

A ———— B

Given: Side A-B

A ———— B

1. Taking A-B as a radius and point A as a center swing a short arc above the center of A-B.

A ———— B

2. With point B as a center swing a short arc across the previous arc to locate point O.

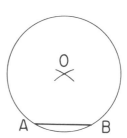

3. With point O as a center draw a circle through points A and B.

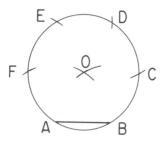

4. Step off length A-B around the circle with a compass to locate points C, D, E, and F.

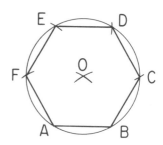

5. Connect points B, C, D, E, F and A to form hexagon.

INFORMATION

At times it may be easier or more convenient to use a draftsman's triangle to aid in the construction of a geometric figure. On page 151 are shown six ways to construct a hexagon. In four of these a 30-60-degree triangle is used. In the other two only a compass and straightedge are needed.

PROBLEM

Construct a hexagon by six different methods.

INSTRUCTIONS

1. Draw the borderlines and title block.

2. Divide the paper into six equal parts.

3. In each part construct one of the hexagons shown on page 151.

4. Use the 30-60-degree triangle only in the constructions where it is indicated.

5. In the other constructions use only compass and straightedge.

Construction No. 14

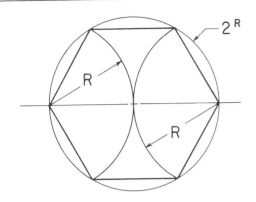

Hexagon inscribed *within* a circle.

Construction No. 15

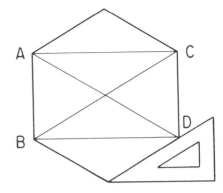

Hexagon with side A-B given.
Hint: Construct rectangle ABCD.

Construction No. 16

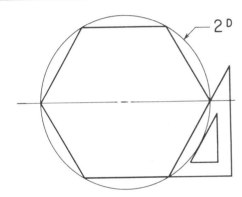

Hexagon inscribed *within* a circle.

Construction No. 17

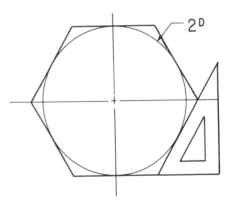

Hexagon circumscribed *about* a circle.

Construction No. 18

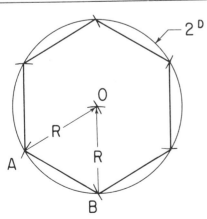

Hexagon with side A-B given.
Hint: Locate O with R = AB and draw a circle.

Construction No. 19

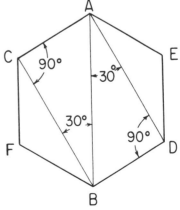

Hexagon on a given long diagonal A-B.
Hint: Construct rectangle ACBD.

INFORMATION

Using only a compass and a straightedge it is possible to construct a five-pointed star or a pentagon.

PROBLEM

Construct a five-pointed star.

INSTRUCTIONS

1. Draw borderlines and title block.

2. Divide the page into two equal parts.

3. In the first part construct a five-pointed star.

4. Follow each step carefully as shown on the following page.

5. The second space will be used for the next figure to be drawn.

Construction No. 20: Construct a five-pointed star or a pentagon.

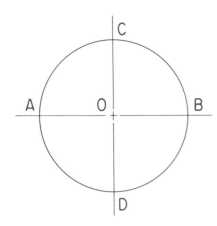

1. Draw a circle with diameter A-B equal to the approximate size of the star that you need. Draw perpendicular bisector C-D.

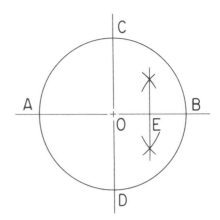

2. Bisect radius O-B at point E.

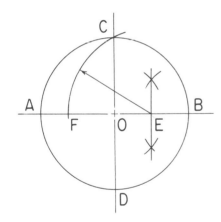

3. With radius E-C and point E as a center, draw an arc cutting A-O at F.

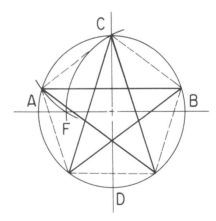

4. The straight-line distance F-C is equal to one-fifth of the circumference of the given circle.
5. With the dividers set to distance F-C, and with C as a starting point, locate the five points on the circle.
6. Draw the lines connecting the points as shown to complete the star.
7. To draw a pentagon, connect points as shown by dashed lines.

INFORMATION

It is worthwhile learning how to draw an approximate ellipse with a T-square, a 30-60-degree triangle and a French curve.

The large axis or major diameter is the longest distance and the small axis or minor diameter is the shortest distance across the ellipse taken through the geometric center.

PROBLEM

Construct an approximate ellipse having given the lengths of the large and small axes.

INSTRUCTIONS

1. Use the second space on the sheet previously prepared for the five-pointed star.

2. Locate the center of this space and using it as a center draw the two circles having diameters equal to the large axis and small axis, respectively.

3. Construct the ellipse.

4. Follow each step carefully.

Construct No. 21: Construct an approximate ellipse.

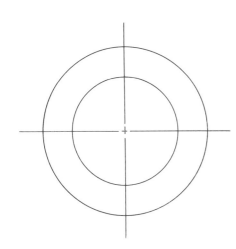

1. Draw two concentric circles. The diameter of the large circle is equal to the length of the large axis of the desired ellipse. The diameter of the small circle is equal to the length of the small axis of the desired ellipse.

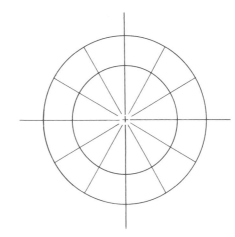

2. Divide the two circles into twelve equal parts. Use your 30-60 degree triangle.

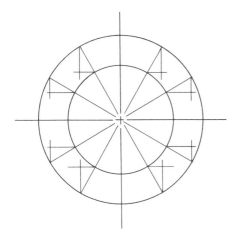

3. Draw horizontal lines from the point where the dividing lines intersect the small circle. Vertical lines are drawn from the point where the dividing lines intersect the large circle.

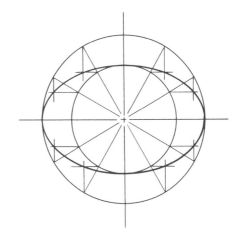

4. Connect the points where the vertical and horizontal lines intersect to complete the ellipse. This may be done free hand, but a much smoother ellipse will be obtained if a French curve is used.

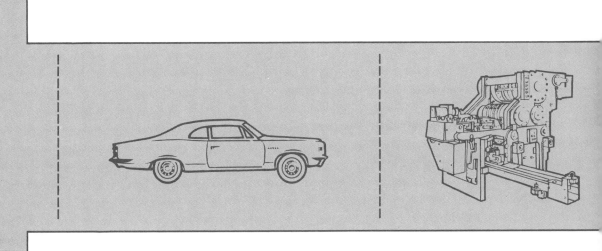

UNIT 13

CONSTRUCTING TANGENTS TO ARCS AND LINES

The purpose of this unit is to show how arcs are drawn tangent to lines at various angles with each other, to a given line and arc, and to two given arcs.

INFORMATION

Frequently it is necessary to connect two lines at an angle with each other by a smooth curve. The easiest way to do this is by drawing a tangent arc. The constructions on pages 159, 160 and 161 show how an exact tangent arc is drawn.

PROBLEM

To draw tangent arcs to two lines at various angles to each other.

INSTRUCTIONS

1. Draw borderlines and title block.

2. Divide drawing space into three equal parts.

3. In the first part, construct an arc tangent to two lines at right angles with each other (see page 159).

4. In the second part, construct an arc tangent to two lines at an acute (less than 90 degrees) angle with each other (see page 160).

5. In the third part, draw an arc tangent to two lines at an obtuse (more than 90 degrees) angle with each other (see page 161).

6. Follow each step carefully and keep construction lines light.

Construction No. 22: Construct a tangent arc to two lines at right angles.

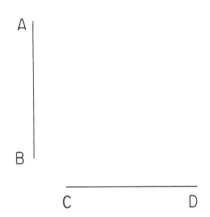

Given: Lines A-B and C-D at right angles to each other.

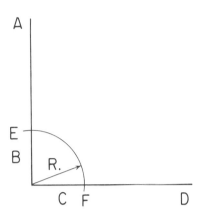

1. Set your compass to any convenient radius and with the intersection of the lines as a center, draw an arc intersecting both lines at point E and F.

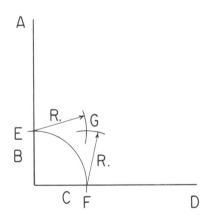

2. With points E and F as centers, draw intersecting arcs of the same radius, R, as the desired tangent arc to locate point G.

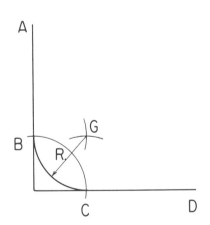

3. With point G as a center and the shortest distance to either line as the radius, draw the tangent arc. To obtain a larger or smaller tangent arc, use a larger or smaller radius, R, respectively in Step 2.

Construction No. 23: Construct a tangent arc to two lines at an acute angle.

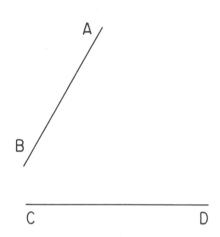

Given: Lines AB and CD at an acute angle with each other.

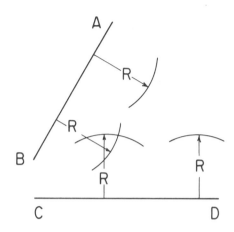

1. Set your compass to desired radius, R, of the tangent arc and near the ends of each line, draw two arcs with their centers on the line.

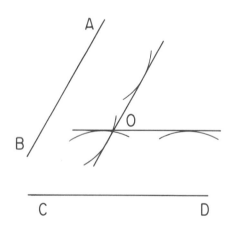

2. Draw straight construction lines tangent to the arcs, as shown.

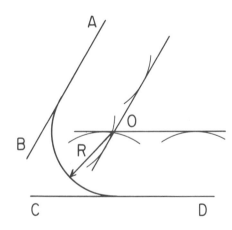

3. The point where these two lines intersect, O, is the center for drawing the required tangent arc. To obtain larger or smaller tangent arc, use larger or smaller radius, R, respectively, in Step 1.

Construction No. 24: Construct a tangent arc to two lines at an obtuse angle.

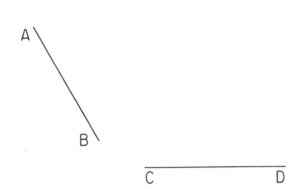

Given: Lines AB and CD at an obtuse angle with each other.

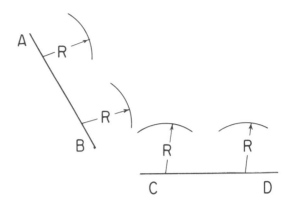

1. Set your compass to desired radius, R, of the tangent arc and near the ends of each line, draw two arcs with their centers on the line.

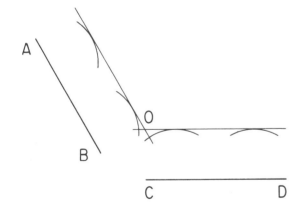

2. Draw straight construction lines tangent to the arcs, as shown.

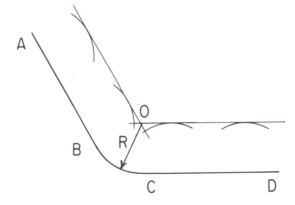

3. The point where these two lines intersect, O, is the center for drawing the required tangent arc. To obtain larger or smaller tangent arc, use larger or smaller radius, R, respectively in Step 1.

INFORMATION

Another construction that the draftsman may have to make from time to time is an arc tangent to another arc and a straight line or to two arcs.

As in the three previous constructions, the purpose is to locate the center of the tangent arc.

PROBLEM

1. Given an arc and a straight line, to draw a connecting arc that is tangent to each.

2. Given two arcs, to draw a connecting arc that is tangent to each.

INSTRUCTIONS

1. Draw borderlines and title block.

2. Divide drawing space into two equal parts.

3. In the first part, construct an arc tangent to a given arc and a given straight line (see page 163).

4. In the second part, construct an arc tangent to two given arcs (see page 164).

5. Follow each step carefully and keep construction lines light.

Construction No. 25: Construct a tangent arc to a given arc and a given line.

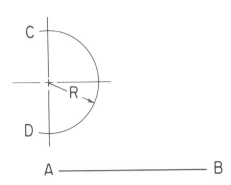

Given: Arc C-D of radius R and line A-B.

1. Line A-B and arc C-D are to be joined by a tangent arc. Let r be the given radius of the desired arc.

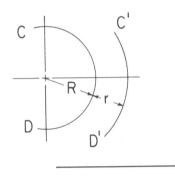

2. Draw arc C'-D' by setting the compass to a radius equal to R + r.

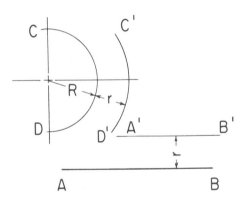

3. Draw line A'-B' at a distance equal to r from, and parallel to, line A-B.

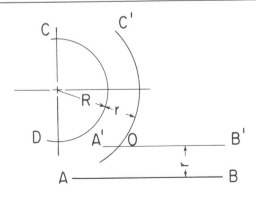

4. The arc C'-D' and the line A'-B' intersect at point O.

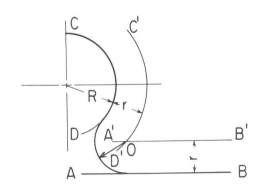

5. With O as a center and with r as a radius, draw the desired arc tangent to the given arc and straight line.

Construction No. 26: Construct a tangent arc to two given arcs.

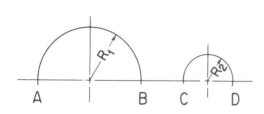

Given: Arcs A-B and C-D of radii R_1 and R_2 respectively.

1. Arcs A-B and C-D are to be joined by a tangent arc. Let r be the given radius of the desired tangent arc.

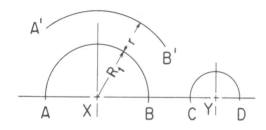

2. Set the compass to a radius equal to R_1 + r. With X as a center, draw arc A'-B'.

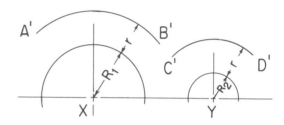

3. Set the compass to a radius equal to R_2 + r. With Y as a center, draw arc C'-D'.

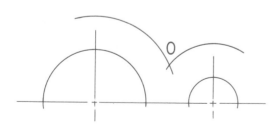

4. The newly drawn arcs intersect at 0 to form the center for the desired tangent arc.

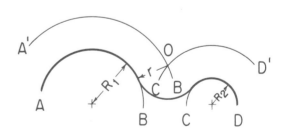

5. Set the compass to radius r. With 0 as center, draw the desired tangent arc.

USING CONSTRUCTIONS IN DRAWINGS

The purpose of this unit is to show how constructions are used in a mechanical drawing.

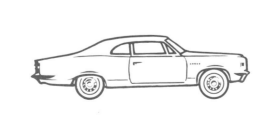
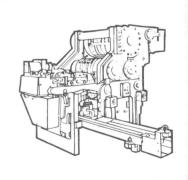

INFORMATION

The ability to carry out the type of constructions previously outlined will often be useful in making mechanical drawings.

PROBLEM

1. Make a one-view drawing of the gasket shown on page 167. Scale: full size.

2. Make a one-view drawing of the washer shown on page 167. Scale: full size. Note, however, that the washer is shown one-half size on page 167.

INSTRUCTIONS

1. Draw borderlines and title block.

2. Make each drawing on a separate sheet of paper.

3. Carefully plan location of each drawing to permit dimensions to be shown without crowding. Note that drawing of gasket should not be centered for this reason.

4. Study drawing to see where constructions are needed and review method, if necessary.

5. *Hint:* Locate centers of and draw all complete circles as a first step.

6. In drawing the gasket note that the two straight lines to the right which form part of the gasket outline are not dimensioned since the length and position of each is determined by the two arcs to which it is tangent.

GASKET

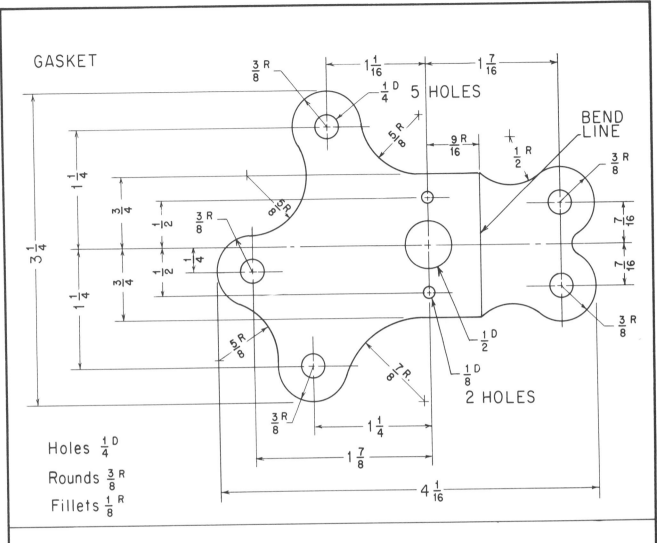

Holes $\frac{1}{4}$ D

Rounds $\frac{3}{8}$ R

Fillets $\frac{1}{8}$ R

WASHER

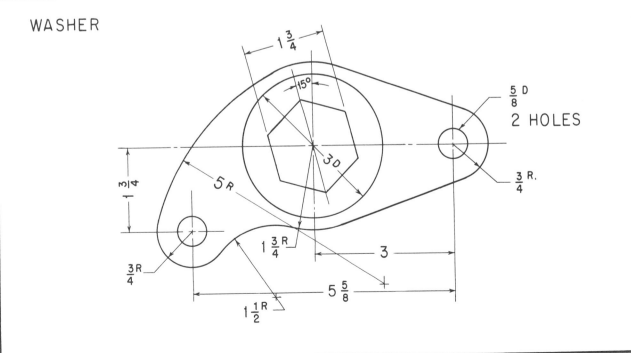

Review Problems

A ——————— B

Problem: Bisect a line AB.

Problem: Draw a hexagon with one side given.

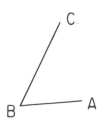

Problem: Bisect an angle ABC.

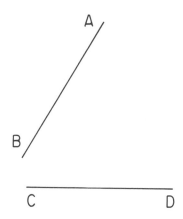

Problem: Draw an arc tangent to the sides of an acute angle. The radius of the arc is 1/2 inch.

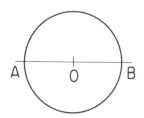

Problem: Draw a regular octagon. Given line AOB.

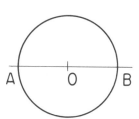

Problem: Draw a regular hexagon. Given line AOB.

Review Questions

Units 11-14 review questions to be answered on a separate sheet of paper.

DIRECTIONS:
For each of the numbered statements below, write the number and after it the figure, symbol, word or words which will complete the sentence. Do NOT write in the book.

1. To bisect a line means divide a line into _____ equal parts.
    a) 2
    b) 4
    c) 6
    d) 8
    e) 3

2. An equilateral triangle is one in which all sides are _____.
    a) perpendicular
    b) oblique
    c) unequal
    d) uneven
    e) equal

3. A hexagon has _____ sides.
    a) 2
    b) 4
    c) 6
    d) 8
    e) 10

4. An octagon has _____ sides.
    a) 2
    b) 4
    c) 6
    d) 5
    e) 8

5. An _____ angle is an angle of less than 90 degrees.
    a) circular
    b) right
    c) perpendicular
    d) acute
    e) obtuse

Review Questions (continued)

6. An _____ angle is an angle of more than 90 degrees.
   a) right
   b) circular
   c) obtuse
   d) acute
   e) perpendicular

7. A square has _____ sides
   a) 2
   b) 4
   c) 6
   d) 8
   e) 10

8. A triangle has _____ sides.
   a) 2
   b) 3
   c) 4
   d) 5
   e) 6

9. A radius is _____ of a diameter.
   a) 1
   b) 1/2
   c) 2
   d) 1/4
   e) 3/4

10. A tangent touches a circle at _____ point(s).
    a) 1
    b) 2
    c) 3
    d) 4
    e) 5

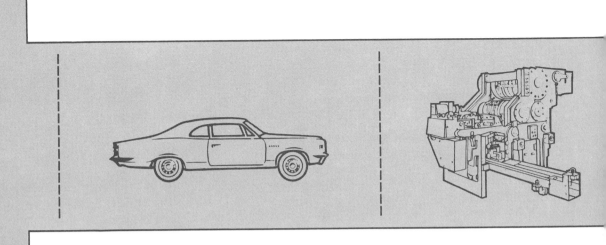

INTRODUCTION TO WORKING DRAWINGS

The purpose of this unit is to teach the meaning of the terms "working drawing", the "mechanics of dimensioning", and the placing of dimensions on working drawings.

In the commercial world, drawings are made for the purpose of manufacturing or constructing useful objects. In order to make an object of any kind the workman must know not only its shape but also its exact size, the materials from which it is to be made, how it is to be finished, and many other items of information which cannot be shown in orthographic views.

INFORMATION

A working drawing is prepared for the purpose of furnishing all necessary information to those persons who must manufacture and assemble the part or machine represented.

The objective is to make this drawing so complete and accurate that little or no supplementary information will be necessary.

The drawing is in orthographic projection with the number of views required to show the needed information.

PROBLEM

Make a complete working drawing of the objects assigned from those shown on pages 173, 174 and 175.

INSTRUCTIONS

1. Draw borderlines and title block. Use one sheet for each object drawn.

2. Decide first upon the number of views required.

3. Lay out these orthographic views in the usual manner. Be careful to allow ample space for dimensions between the views and between the views and borderlines.

4. Dimension the top view first, beginning with the lengthwise dimensions.

   a. Draw lines from the points you intend to dimension, then draw the dimension lines, making breaks in the lines for the figures.

   b. Place the detail dimensions nearest the object and the overall dimension outside the detail dimensions. This prevents any crossing of dimension lines.

   c. Draw the arrow heads and insert the proper figures, thus completing the dimensions for length.

5. Proceed in the same manner for the width dimensions of the object, placing them in their proper positions. This completes the dimensioning of the top view.

6. Take the front view next, and proceed as before, giving the heights of all steps.

Practice in Making Working Drawings—1

Dimension drawings completely. Use a sharp 2H pencil for dimension lines, extension lines, and center lines. Use a sharp F pencil for arrowheads and lettering.

Space dimensions 1/4 inch from object outline and 1/4 inch apart. Use complete guide lines (4H) pencil) for all dimension figures and notes. Make whole numbers and capitals 1/8 inch high, fractions 1/4 inch high.

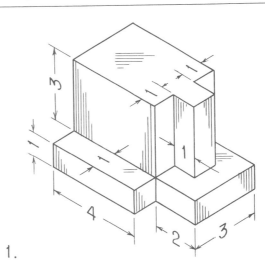

1.

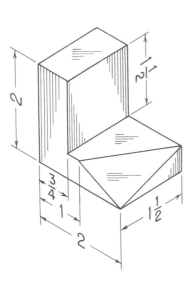

2.

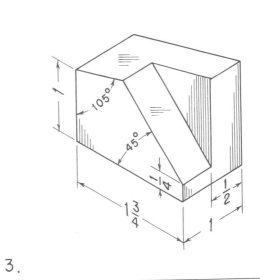

3.

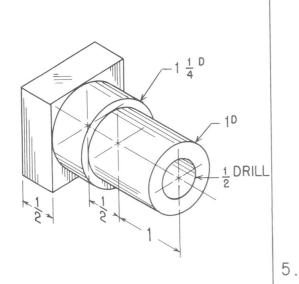

4.

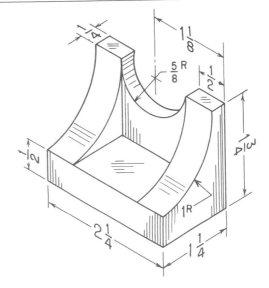

5.

Practice in Making Working Drawings—2

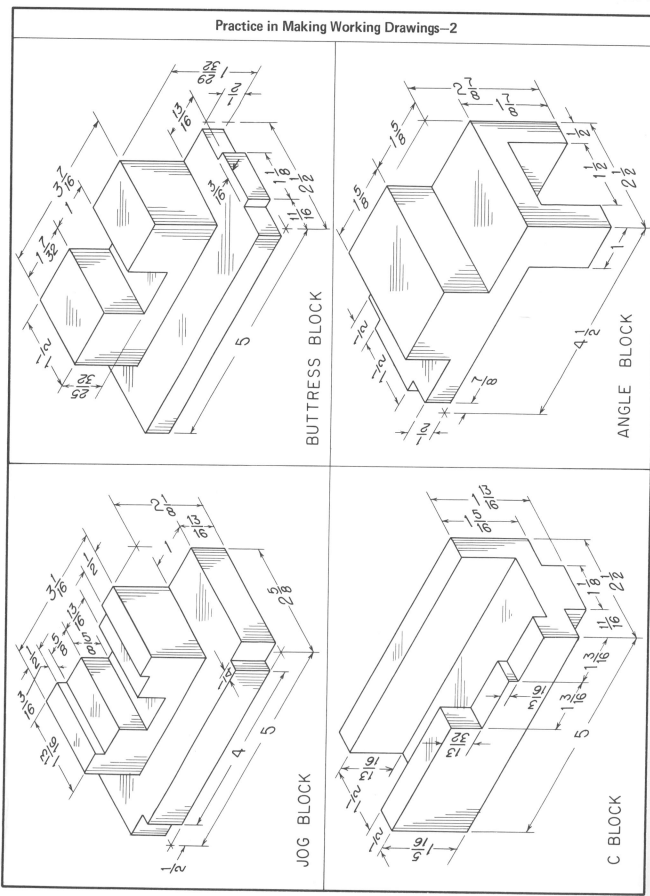

BUTTRESS BLOCK

ANGLE BLOCK

JOG BLOCK

C BLOCK

Practice in Making Working Drawings—3

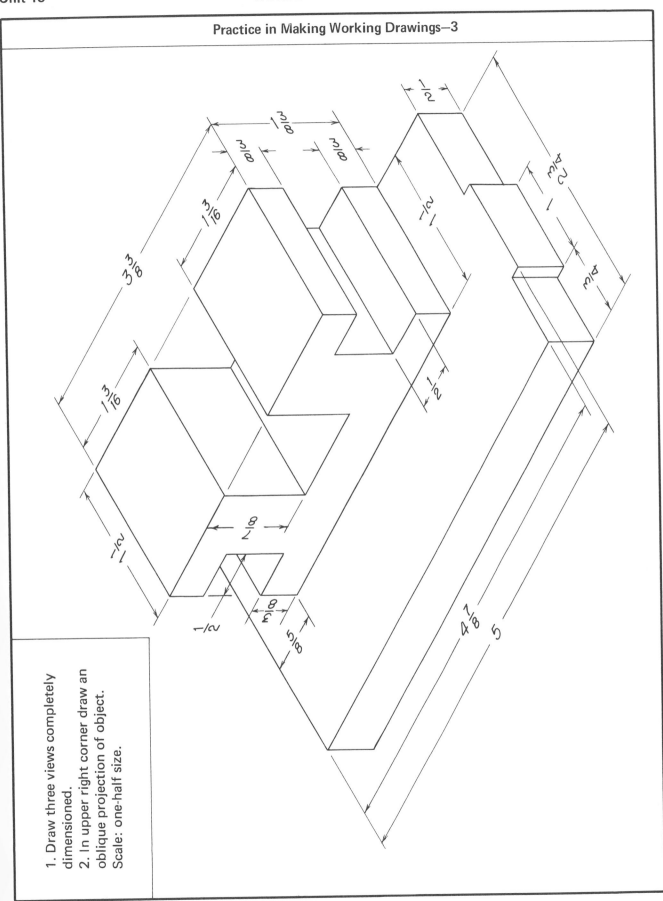

1. Draw three views completely dimensioned.
2. In upper right corner draw an oblique projection of object. Scale: one-half size.

Review Questions

Unit 15 review questions to be answered on a separate sheet of paper.

DIRECTIONS:

For each of the numbered statements below, write the number and after it the figure, symbol, word or words which will complete the sentence. Do NOT write in the book.

1. We must add _____ to an orthographic view to make a working drawing.
   a) arrows
   b) views
   c) dimensions
   d) statements
   e) sections

2. Dimensions are read from bottom and _____ side.
   a) top
   b) front
   c) bottom
   d) right
   e) left

3. A dimension is _____ placed on a view.
   a) always
   b) never
   c) positively
   d) fractionally
   e) correctly

4. The weight of a dimension line is _____ compared to object lines.
   a) medium
   b) lighter
   c) heavier
   d) softer
   e) similar

5. The first dimension line should be _____ inch away from the object.
   a) 1/2
   b) 1/8
   c) 1/4
   d) 1/16
   e) 3/16

6. Extension lines _____ touch dimension lines.
   a) always
   b) sometimes
   c) must
   d) never
   e) couldn't

7. The height dimension is shown in the _____ view or right side view.
   a) top
   b) oblique
   c) front
   d) bottom
   e) isometric

8. Space between views should be at least _____ inch.
   a) 1/8
   b) 1/4
   c) 3/16
   d) 3/8
   e) 1

9. Dimensions are _____ repeated on a working drawing.
   a) sometimes
   b) never
   c) always
   d) positively
   e) correctly

10. A hidden feature is _____ dimensioned on a working drawing.
    a) always
    b) never
    c) rarely
    d) often
    e) sometimes

FREEHAND SKETCHING

The purpose of this unit is to show how to make a good freehand sketch. Sketching is probably the most widely used form of drawing. It shows what an object looks like, and how it is made.

Most ideas are usually expressed first as a freehand sketch and later translated into finished instrument drawings. A person who can produce a clear and accurate sketch possesses a valuable means of imparting information which aids production efficiency.

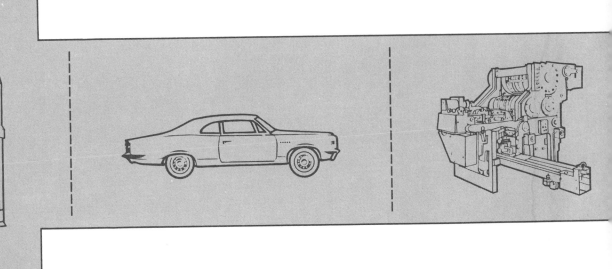

INFORMATION

For freehand sketching a medium F or soft HB pencil is best. The pencil should have a long conical point.

Hold the pencil well back from the end, 2 inches or more. Support the hand lightly upon the last two fingers. Make the lines all of light or medium weight and uniform thickness.

The basic information about blueprints applies to sketching as well.

PROBLEM

Make a sketch of the objects assigned from the following groups.

INSTRUCTIONS

1. Draw border lines and title block.

2. Divide paper into twelve equal boxes.

3. In each box sketch lines, angle and square as shown.

4. The use of cross-section paper saves time.

5. When erasing is required, artgum and pink pearl types are best; they will do a cleaner job of removing pencil lines from paper.

How to Sketch Straight Lines

1. Horizontal lines are drawn from left to right. Mark off two points spaced a distance equal to the length of line.

2. Vertical lines are drawn from top to bottom. Mark off two points spaced a distance equal to the length of the line to be drawn.

3. Lines inclined upward from left to right are drawn from bottom to top as shown.

4. Lines inclined upward from right to left are drawn from bottom to top as shown.

How to Sketch Angles

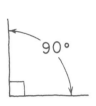

1. Draw two lines to form a right angle.

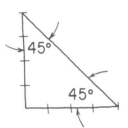

2. Mark off an equal number of units on both lines and connect the last unit of each line to form a 45° angle.

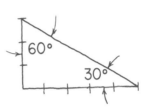

3. Mark off three units on one line and five units on the other line to form a 30°-60° angles.

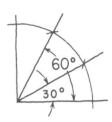

4. Sketch a quarter circle and divide the arc into three parts thus forming 30°-60° angles.

How to Sketch a Square

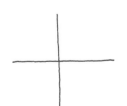

1. Draw a vertical and a horizontal line through a point locating center of square.

2. Space off equal distances on these lines.

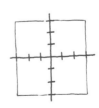

3. Sketch light horizontal and vertical lines through the outer points to form the square.

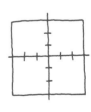

4. Darken the lines to form the square.

How to Sketch an Arc

1. Sketch a right (90-degree) angle.

2. Mark off units on each leg of the angle equal in length to the radius of the desired arc.

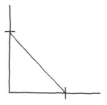

3. Connect these points with a construction line.

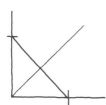

4. Mark the halfway point on the construction lines. Sketch a diagonal through this dividing point.

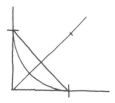

5. Mark off a point halfway between the diagonal line and the intersection of the legs of the angle. Sketch an arc through the three points as shown.

6. Erase all unnecessary guidelines and darken the curve and necessary adjoining straight lines.

How to Sketch a Circle

1. Draw a vertical and a horizontal line through a point making the center of the desired circle.

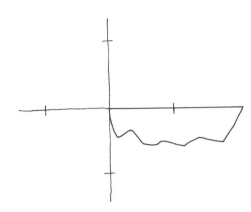

2. Along a straight edge of a piece of scrap paper mark off the desired radius. Place one end of this marked-off radius at the center point and mark off the radius on each intersecting line.

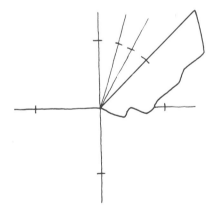

3. Draw diagonal lines at various intervals in between these lines to locate the outer radial points, using the scrap paper.

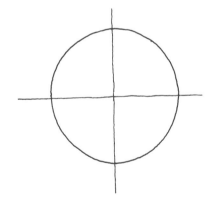

4. Complete the circle by drawing short arcs through one quadrant at a time. Darken the completed circle.

INFORMATION

The easiest way to copy, enlarge, or reduce the size of a drawing is by the graph method. The original drawing is blocked off into 1/8-inch squares and is sketched freehand into squares of the same size (for copying), larger squares (for enlarging), or smaller squares (for reducing).

PROBLEMS

1. Enlarge smaller drawing of the bracket on page 185 to twice its original size.

2. Copy each of the objects shown on page 186 to same size.

INSTRUCTIONS

1. Draw borderlines and title block.

2. Draw squares lightly, 1/2-inch for enlarging the drawing on page 185 and 1/4-inch for copying the drawings on page 186.

3. Number horizontal and vertical lines as shown.

4. Transfer points where the original drawing crosses the squares to the same points on the new set of squares. Then, draw in the figure freehand.

Enlarging by the Graph Method

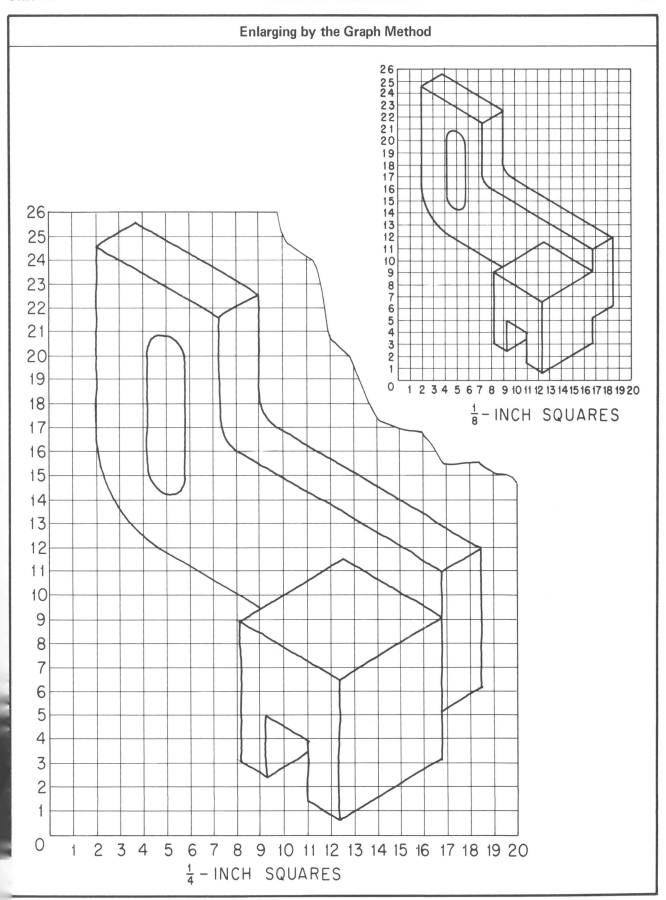

$\frac{1}{8}$- INCH SQUARES

$\frac{1}{4}$- INCH SQUARES

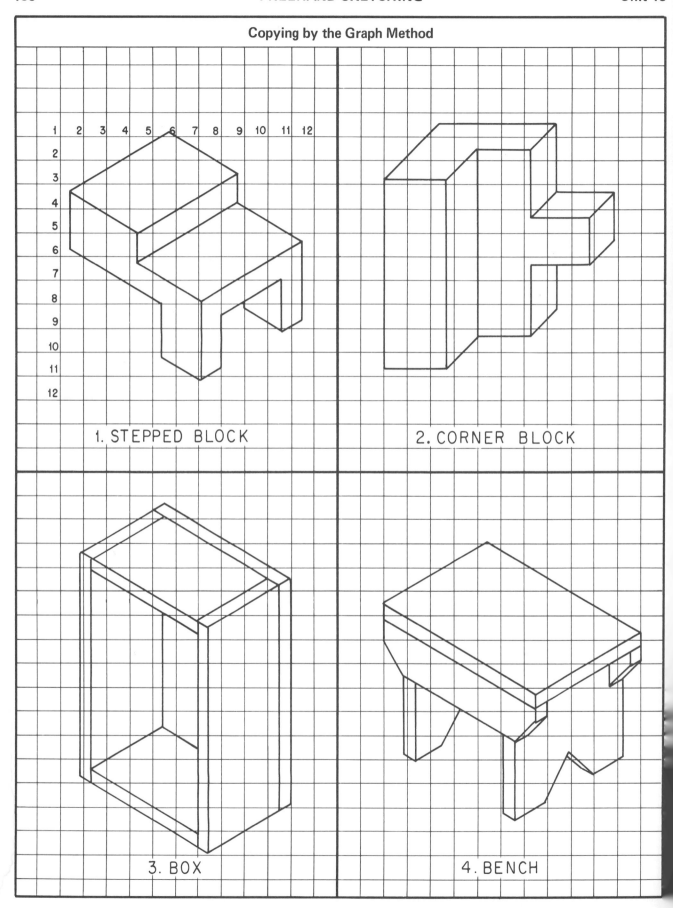

Copying by the Graph Method

1. STEPPED BLOCK

2. CORNER BLOCK

3. BOX

4. BENCH

Review Questions

Unit 16 review questions to be answered on a separate sheet of paper.

DIRECTIONS:

For each of the numbered statements below, write the number and after it the figure, symbol, word or words which will complete the sentence. Do NOT write in the book.

1. It is usually better to sketch with cross-_____ paper.
   a) bow
   b) way
   c) section
   d) length
   e) list

2. For freehand sketching a medium F or soft _____ pencil is best.
   a) 4H
   b) 6H
   c) 5H
   d) 3H
   e) HB

3. Horizontal lines are drawn from left to _____ in freehand sketching.
   a) right
   b) side
   c) rear
   d) top
   e) bottom

4. Vertical lines are drawn from _____ to bottom in freehand sketching.
   a) side
   b) front
   c) back
   d) top
   e) rear

5. Inclined lines from left to right are drawn from _____ to top in freehand sketching.
   a) bottom
   b) side
   c) rear
   d) back
   e) top

Review Questions (continued)

6. Inclined lines from right to left are drawn from _____ to top in freehand sketching.
   a) rear
   b) bottom
   c) side
   d) back
   e) top

7. The easiest way to enlarge or reduce the size of a drawing is by the _____ method.
   a) parallel
   b) isometric
   c) oblique
   d) graph
   e) orthographic

8. Freehand sketching is the technique of making a drawing without the use of _____.
   a) slides
   b) photos
   c) letters
   d) instruments
   e) ink

9. In freehand sketching the pencil should have a long _____ point.
   a) straight
   b) chiseled
   c) flat
   d) round
   e) conical

10. In sketching lines place a/an _____ where you want the line to begin and one where you want it to end.
    a) arrow
    b) arc
    c) dot
    d) dimension
    e) circle

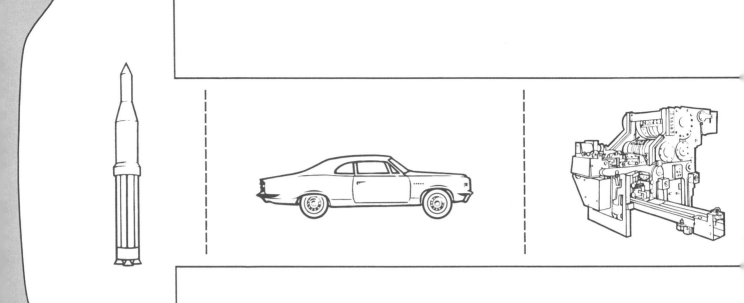

INTERPRETATION

The purpose of this unit is to show how a pictorial drawing can be drawn from an orthographic drawing.

In addition to being able to visualize how objects look, you will find it useful to know how sketches of them are actually drawn. If you and a fellow worker are discussing a detail drawing having three views, you can make your point clear by sketching a picture which the detail drawing represents.

In the previous sections you have learned how mechanical drawings are made. You have observed that a mechanical drawing may have one, two, or three views; each view being determined by the observation point of a person who is looking directly at one of the three surfaces—top, front or side. A pictorial drawing, on the other hand, shows the appearance of an object from a given angle, so that you see several surfaces at the same time from one viewpoint.

INFORMATION

Often an engineer or draftsman must sketch an object pictorially in order to present an idea to someone who has not been trained to read a multiview (orthographic) drawing. In design work, a pictorial view frequently is placed on a preliminary sketch along with the dimensional views, so that anyone assisting in the development of the design may be able quickly to grasp an idea of the pictorial form visualized by the designer.

PROBLEM

Make an isometric drawing of the steel block on page 191.

INSTRUCTIONS

1. Draw border lines and title block.

2. Follow the steps shown.

Making an Isometric Sketch from an Orthographic Drawing—2

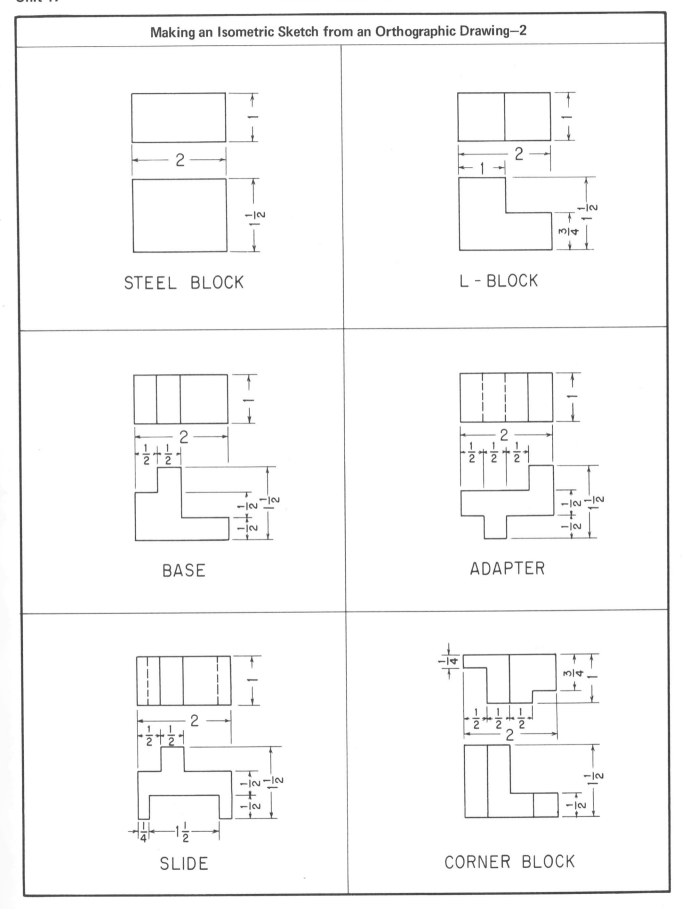

STEEL BLOCK

L - BLOCK

BASE

ADAPTER

SLIDE

CORNER BLOCK

INFORMATION

Remember that isometric drawings are built up on what are called isometric axes. These axes make an angle of 120 degrees with each other and 30 degrees with the horizontal.

PROBLEM

Make an isometric drawing from the orthographic drawings of the support and corner block shown on the facing page.

INSTRUCTIONS

1. Draw borderlines and title block.

2. Divide paper into two equal parts.

3. In the first part make an isometric drawing of the support.

4. In the second part make an isometric drawing of the corner block.

Making an Isometric Sketch from an Orthographic Drawing—3

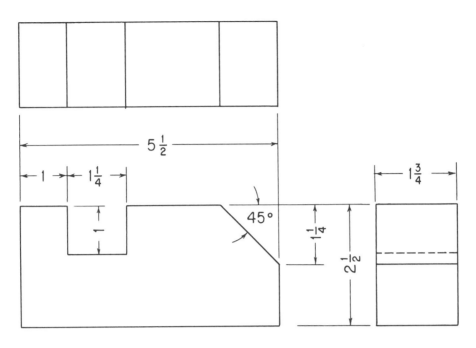

SUPPORT

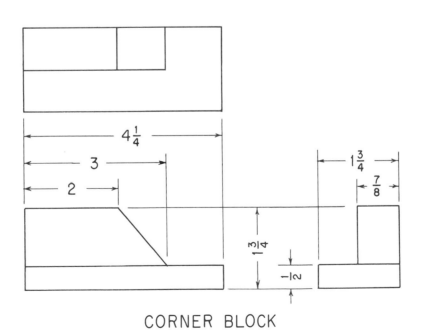

CORNER BLOCK

INFORMATION

Continued practice in making isometric sketches from orthographic drawings will develop speed and confidence.

PROBLEM

Make an isometric drawing from each of the orthographic drawings shown on the facing page.

INSTRUCTIONS

1. Draw borderlines and title block.

2. Divide drawing space into two equal parts.

3. In the first part make an isometric sketch of the splay block.

4. In the second part make an isometric sketch of the point block.

5. On a second sheet of paper follow the same procedure for the support block and the miter block.

Making an Isometric Sketch from an Orthographic Drawing—4

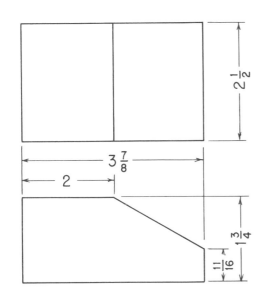

SPLAY BLOCK

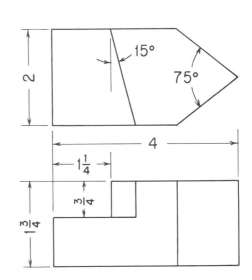

POINT BLOCK

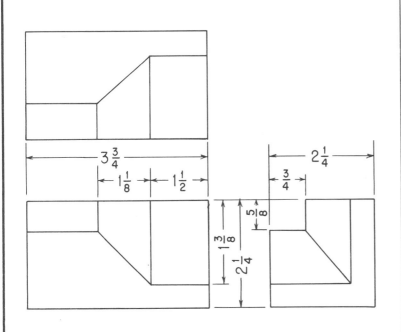

SUPPORT BLOCK

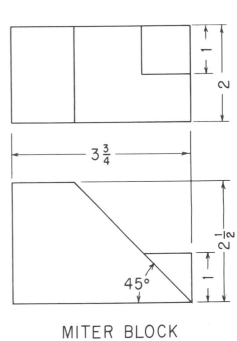

MITER BLOCK

INFORMATION

The ability to change an orthographic drawing to a pictorial drawing is useful in clarifying details which would be difficult to visualize.

A pictorial drawing used in drafting is the oblique drawing. An oblique drawing has a front surface which is shown in its true size and shape, and a top and side which usually slant back at an angle of 45 degrees with the horizontal but can be 30 degrees or 60 degrees. In this book 45 degrees is used.

PROBLEM

Make an oblique drawing of a block from the orthographic drawing shown on the following page.

INSTRUCTIONS

1. Draw border lines and title block.

2. Draw true front view then draw all oblique lines parallel to each other at 45 degrees.

Making an Oblique Sketch from an Orthographic Drawing—1

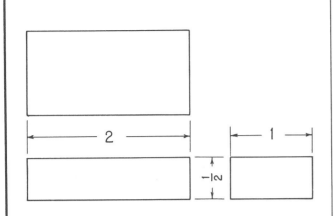

THREE-VIEW DRAWING OF A BLOCK

Let us suppose that you want to make a picture sketch of a block 2 inches long, 1 inch wide, and 1/2 inch in height or thickness. The procedure is as follows:

1. Draw the front view 2 inches long by 1/2 inch high.

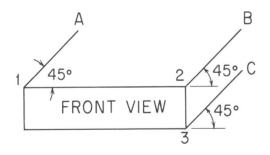

2. Next draw the slant lines to A, B, and C from 1, 2, and 3. These lines are all drawn at the same angle from the horizontal. We have chosen the angle of 45 degrees but any convenient angle may be used in a freehand sketch.

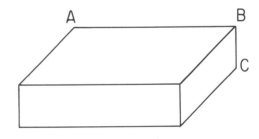

PICTORIAL DRAWING OF BLOCK

3. If the slant lines to A, B, and C are drawn 1 inch long, the same length as the actual width of the object, the drawing may be called an oblique drawing. If they are reduced in the drawing to one-half of their true length on the object, the sketch may be called a cabinet type of oblique drawing. Cabinet drawings appear to be more in proportion to the object than do oblique drawings.

INFORMATION

Oblique sketches accomplish about the same purpose as isometric sketches; the chief difference being that in oblique projection, one of the surfaces of the part is shown in true form and proportion, that is, as the surface would be drawn orthographically if parallel with the plane of projection. The figure on page 199 shows the oblique axes and an object sketched upon them.

PROBLEM

Make an oblique drawing from each of the orthographic drawings shown on the following page.

INSTRUCTIONS

1. Draw border lines and title block.

2. Divide a sheet of paper into two equal parts.

3. In the first part make an oblique drawing of the first object on page 201.

4. In the second part make an oblique drawing of the second object.

5. Repeat this same procedure on the second and third sheets for the remaining objects.

Making an Oblique Sketch from an Orthographic Drawing—2

1.

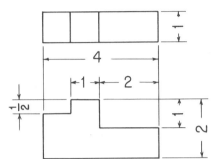

2.

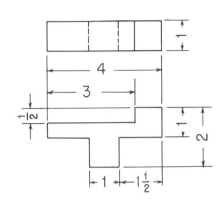

3.

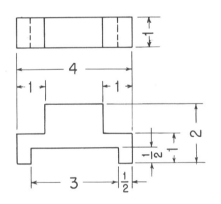

4.

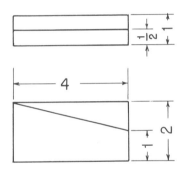

5.

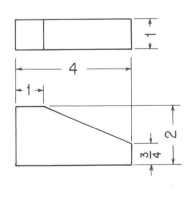

6.

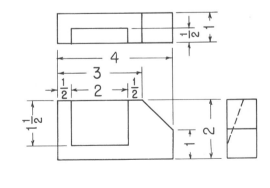

Review Questions

Unit 17 review questions to be answered on a separate sheet of paper.

DIRECTIONS:

For each of the numbered statements below, write the number and after it the figure, symbol, word or words which will complete the sentence. Do NOT write in the book.

1. A/an _____ drawing shows the true size and shape of an object.
    a) oblique
    b) isometric
    c) orthographic
    d) auxiliary
    e) perspective

2. A/an _____ drawing shows several surfaces from one viewpoint at the same time.
    a) oblique
    b) pictorial
    c) geometric
    d) mechanical
    e) detail

3. A sketch of an object is a/an _____ drawing.
    a) photograph
    b) diagrammatic
    c) auxiliary
    d) pictorial
    e) detail

4. The construction angle of an isometric drawing is _____ degrees.
    a) 20
    b) 30
    c) 45
    d) 60
    e) 90

5. The construction angle of an oblique drawing is _____ degrees.
    a) 20
    b) 30
    c) 45
    d) 90
    e) 60

6. One type of pictorial drawing is called _____.
   a) orthographic
   b) working
   c) isometric
   d) auxiliary
   e) development

7. The isometric "Y" axis is made up of three lines drawn: _____
   a) one vertical, two horizontal
   b) three horizontal
   c) one horizontal, two vertical
   d) two at 30 degrees, one vertical
   e) two 45 degree lines, one vertical

8. Any line not parallel to the isometric axis is called a _____ line.
   a) symmetrical
   b) oblique
   c) isometric
   d) non-isometric
   e) parallel

9. An isometric line is a line that is _____ to the isometric axis.
   a) symmetrical
   b) slanted
   c) parallel
   d) oblique
   e) perpendicular

10. The word "isometric" means _____.
    a) inclined
    b) slanted
    c) symmetrical
    d) equal measure
    e) unequal

UNIT 18

INKING-
INSTRUMENTS

The purpose of this unit is to show how to make
a good ink drawing. The pencil line is limited
for reproduction in that it will not show a clear,
sharp, dark, smooth line.

It is necessary to have an ink drawing if it is to
be reduced for microfilming or printed, either
from an engraving or by lithographing. For example, drawings for an instruction manual to
be used with a piece of equipment or machinery
should be inked for good reproduction.

When the time comes to make drawings for reproduction, it is to the student's advantage to
have some knowledge and skill in ink drawing.

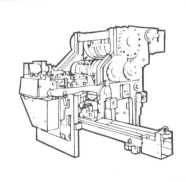

INFORMATION

Two kinds of ink drawing pens are commonly used in mechanical drafting. One type has a round stylus and carries an ink supply in the barrel. A different stylus is used for each width of line. This type of pen is shown at the top of page 207. The other type is the standard ruling pen shown on page 208. Ink is inserted between the drawing points with a dropper stopper. The distance between the points may be changed with a thumb adjusting screw to obtain different widths of line.

Circles and arcs are drawn with a bow compass having adjustable points similar to those in a ruling pen. One of these is shown at the bottom of page 207.

PROBLEM

To become familiar with ink drawing instruments and their use.

INSTRUCTIONS

1. Study carefully the information about ink drawing instruments given on pages 207 and 208.

2. Practice drawing both straight lines and arcs and circles using the ink drawing instruments set to a series of different line widths.

3. Now compare your practice lines with those shown on page 209. If any of your lines are poorly drawn, note the cause given.

4. Again draw a set of straight and curved lines of different thicknesses paying careful attention to the instructions given on pages 207 and 208.

Using a Mechanical Pen and Bow Compass

One type of mechanical pen that is widely used is called a Rapidograph. It can be used for drawing as well as lettering. The point is a round stylus and each size, numbers 00, 0, 1, 2, and 3, draws a different line thickness. The Rapidograph can carry a large amount of India ink so that it does not have to be filled as often as the ordinary ruling pen. The Rapidograph may also be used with lettering templates.

Courtesy of Kohinoor, Inc.

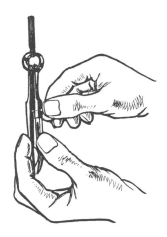
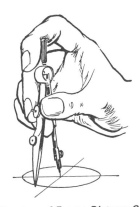

Courtesy of Eugene Dietzgen Co.

Bow instruments are used in the same manner as the compasses and dividers, except that their use is confined to small dimensions. They are somewhat similar in design except that the legs have a spring head or joint and are adjusted by means of an adjusting screw.

Using the Ruling Pen

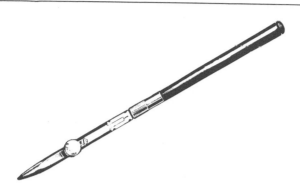

1. The ruling pen is used for inking all lines other than circular ones.

2. Drawing ink is available in bottles with a dropper stopper, or it may be purchased in tubes. Care should be taken not to put too much ink in the pen.

3. The pen should be held with the adjusting screw away from the body, the handle resting against the first finger, and the thumb and second in such a position as to permit turning the adjusting screw.

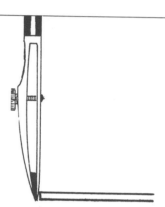

4. In ruling lines the pen should be held in a nearly vertical position against the straight edge with the points parallel to the edge and the handle inclined slightly to the front.

5. The points of the ruling pen should have an oval or elliptical shape.

6. After considerable use the points of the pen become worn and it is often necessary to sharpen them on a Pumice stone.

Illustrations courtesy of Eugene Dietzgen Co.

Types of Lines	Faulty Ruling
1. Visible outline	1. Blade tip too close to the T-square edge. Ink ran under. Avoid sloping in.
2. Hidden outline	2. Pen blade sloped away from the T-square. This causes raggedness of top of line.
3. Center line	3. Lint between the pen blades cause a ragged line. Wipe often with chamois skin.
4. Dimension line	4. Too much ink in the pen, beginning of the line too heavy. Use about 1/4 inch of ink in pen.
5. Extension line	5. Ink on outside of pen blade ran under. Keep the outside of the pen blades clean.
6. Cutting plane	6. Don't use a blotter on drawing ink. Give it sufficient time to dry.
7. Short break	7. Insufficient ink to finish the line. Always fill the ruling pen adequately.
8. Section lining	8. The ruling pen permitted to wobble. Hold it parallel to the T-square.

INFORMATION

On the next page is an actual test that was given to applicants in order to determine their ability to make an ink drawing.

PROBLEM

Make a pencil drawing of the Clamp Block on page **211**, then make an ink drawing of the same.

INSTRUCTIONS

Draw border lines and title block.

Use a definite procedure in inking a drawing.

1. Dust drawing table and wipe instruments before starting work.

2. Draw arcs of circles.

3. With compass draw large circles.

4. With bow compass draw small circles.

5. With French curve draw irregular curves.

6. With ruling pen draw horizontal lines.

7. With ruling pen draw vertical lines.

8. With ruling pen draw slanting lines.

9. Draw section lines.

10. Draw dimensions and arrows.

11. Letter notes and title.

12. Draw border.

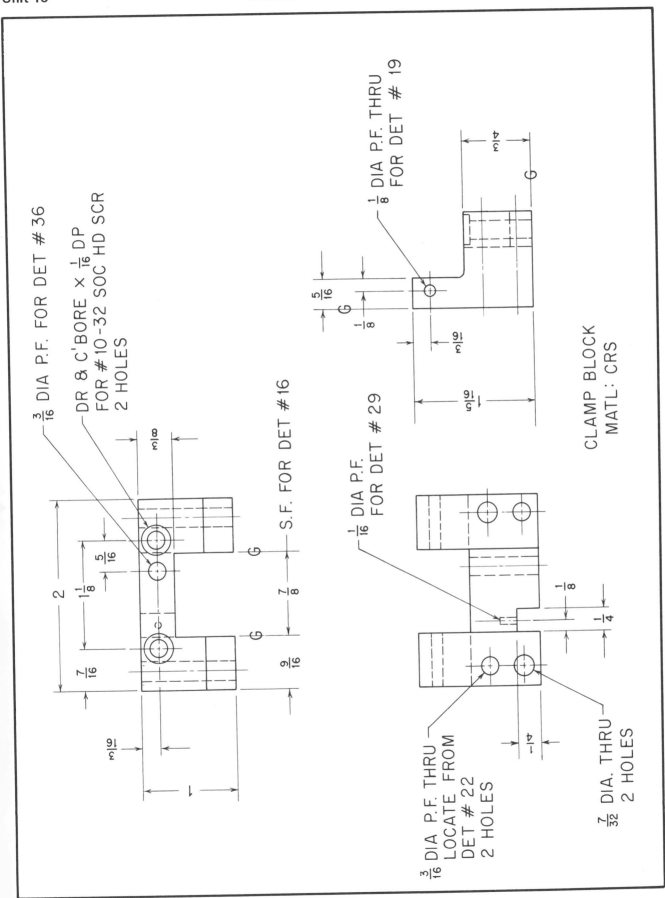

$\frac{3}{16}$ DIA P.F. FOR DET # 36

DR & C'BORE × $\frac{1}{16}$ DP FOR #10-32 SOC HD SCR 2 HOLES

S.F. FOR DET #16

$\frac{1}{8}$ DIA P.F. THRU FOR DET # 19

CLAMP BLOCK
MATL: CRS

$\frac{1}{16}$ DIA P.F. FOR DET # 29

$\frac{3}{16}$ DIA P.F. THRU LOCATE FROM DET # 22 2 HOLES

$\frac{7}{32}$ DIA. THRU 2 HOLES

Review Questions

Unit 18 review questions to be answered on a separate sheet of paper.

DIRECTIONS:

For each of the numbered statements below, write the number and after it the figure, symbol, word or words which will complete the sentence. Do NOT write in the book.

1. The ruling pen is used for inking all lines other than _____ ones.
   a) ragged
   b) circular
   c) straight
   d) deep
   e) irregular

2. Drawing ink is available in bottles and _____.
   a) crayon
   b) charcoal
   c) pens
   d) cake
   e) tubes

3. The pen should be held with the _____ screw away from the body.
   a) rigid
   b) straight
   c) adjusting
   d) regular
   e) light

4. The points of the ruling pen should have a/an _____ or elliptical shape.
   a) straight
   b) round
   c) vertical
   d) square
   e) oval

5. A blade tip too close to the T-square edge causes ink to _____ under.
   a) run
   b) stop
   c) coagulate
   d) join
   e) dry

Review Questions (continued)

6. Lint between the pen blades cause a/an ___ ___ line.
   a) straight
   b) curved
   c) ragged
   d) deep
   e) round

7. Rapidograph pens can be used for drawing as well as _____.
   a) speed
   b) building
   c) instruments
   d) lettering
   e) geometry

8. Bow instruments are used in the same manner as _____.
   a) pens
   b) instruments
   c) nibs
   d) compasses
   e) illustrations

9. Begin an inking drawing by drawing _____ of circles.
   a) lines
   b) tangents
   c) arcs
   d) circumference
   e) radius

10. A blotter should _____ be used in inking drawing.
    a) always
    b) definitely
    c) not
    d) sometimes
    e) irregularly

UNIT 19

ISOMETRIC CIRCLES AND ARCS

The purpose of this unit is to show how circles are drawn in isometric projection.

In an isometric drawing a circle appears as an ellipse. Also, in an isometric drawing an arc of a circle is drawn as a corresponding part of an ellipse. Since an ellipse is difficult to draw exactly, in isometric projection an approximation is constructed using four circular arcs.

INFORMATION

This is a step-by-step explanation of how to construct an isometric circle (actually an approximate ellipse) using the 4-center method.

PROBLEM

Draw an isometric circle using the 4-center method in your graph notebook.

INSTRUCTIONS

1. Follow each step carefully as explained on the facing page.

2. Use a 4H pencil for all construction lines and an H pencil for the outline of the isometric circle.

3. Practice this method of drawing isometric circles so that you can construct them without referring to the text.

Constructing an Isometric Circle in Horizontal Position

Given: A circle of a specified diameter.

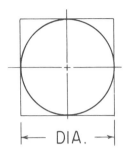

← DIA. →

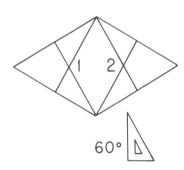

1. Draw a square in isometric projection with sides equal in length to the diameter of the given circle.

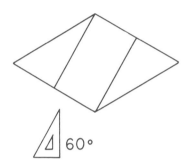

60°

2. Draw two lines from the upper and lower corners at an angle of 60 degrees with the horizontal as shown. These will intersect the opposite sides at the points where the arcs are to be drawn tangent to them.

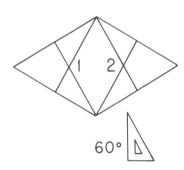

60°

3. Draw two more lines from the upper and lower corners also at 60 degrees with the horizontal as shown to locate points 1 and 2.

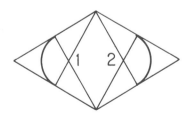

4. With 1 and 2 as centers draw small arcs tangent to the sides of the square.

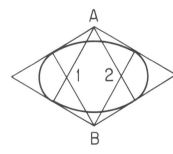

5. With A and B as centers draw large arcs tangent to the sides of the square.

INFORMATION

When two or more circles of the same diameter occur in parallel planes and their centers lie along a common straight line perpendicular to these parallel planes, the construction may be simplified. Thus, the figures on the facing page show how an isometric drawing of a cylinder is made. The centers for the ellipse representing the top are found in the usual way, while the four centers for the base are located by moving the centers at the top downward a distance equal to the height of the cylinder. It should be noted that corresponding centers lie along isometric lines parallel to the axis of the cylinder.

PROBLEM

Make an isometric drawing of the cylinder shown on the facing page.

Scale: full size.

INSTRUCTIONS

1. Draw borderlines and title block.

2. First draw the isometric square and locate the arc centers.

3. Then draw the isometric circle.

4. Project vertically downward from each of the four centers.

5. Locate new centers and draw the isometric circle.

6. Connect both circles with tangent lines.

7. Darken object lines.

8. Omit hidden lines and dimensions.

9. Do not erase construction lines.

Constructing a Vertical Isometric Cylinder

Given: A cylinder of a specified size.

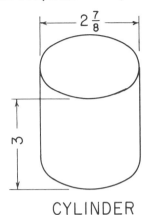

CYLINDER

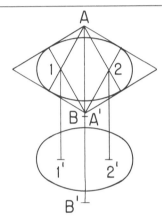

1. Draw an isometric circle for the top by the four-center system after first drawing a horizontal isometric square.

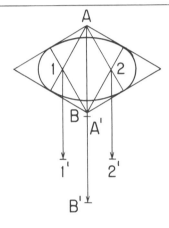

2. Project vertically downward from each point, 1, 2, A and B, a distance equal to the height of the cylinder. Use a compass set to the length of the cylinder to mark off this length to establish four new corners.

3. Swing arcs from new centers 1', 2', A' and B' respectively equal to those swung from centers 1, 2, A and B.

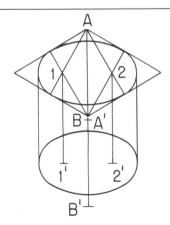

4. Drop the two vertical sides as shown.

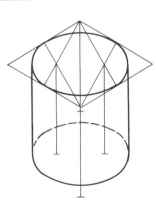

5. Darken visible object lines to complete the drawing.

PROBLEM

Make an isometric drawing of the horizontal cylinder shown on the facing page.

Scale: full size.

INSTRUCTIONS

1. Draw border lines and title block.

2. Draw light vertical and horizontal construction lines locating the four centers of all circles and arcs.

3. Follow the step-by-step method shown for construction of the cylinder.

4. Omit dimension and hidden lines.

5. Do not erase construction lines.

Constructing a Horizontal Isometric Cylinder

Given: A cylinder of a specified size.

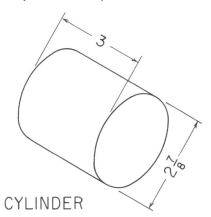

CYLINDER

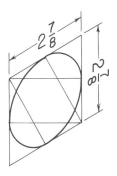

1. Draw isometric circle by the four-center system after first drawing a vertical isometric square.

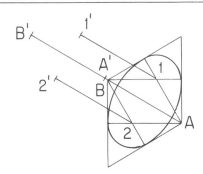

2. Project backward, at an angle of 30° with horizontal, from each point 1, 2, A, and B, a distance equal to the length of the cylinder to establish four new centers. *Note:* A compass is set to the length of the cylinder and using points 1, 2, A and B successively as centers, this length is marked off on the projection lines.

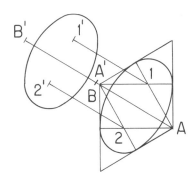

3. Swing arcs from new centers 1', 2', A' and B' to complete the ellipse.

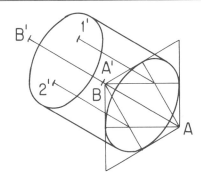

4. Draw the sides at an angle of 30° with the horizontal.

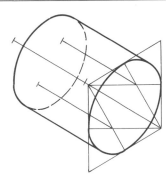

5. Darken visible object lines to complete the drawing.

INFORMATION

As has been shown, isometric circles appear elliptical in shape and can be readily approximated by four arcs drawn with a compass. The series of figures on the following page shows how isometric circles are constructed in three planes at right angles to each other.

PROBLEM

Draw a 3-inch isometric cube and construct an isometric circle on each of its sides.

INSTRUCTIONS

1. Draw borderlines and title block.

2. Center 3-inch isometric cube within the drawing space.

3. Use a 4H pencil for construction lines and an H pencil for object lines.

4. Do not erase construction lines.

Drawing Isometric Circles in Three Planes

To construct isometric circles on the three visible faces of an isometric cube.

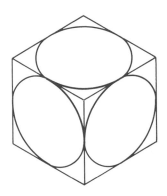

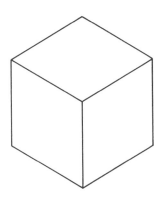

1. Construct an isometric cube with the length of each edge equal to the diameter of the required circles.

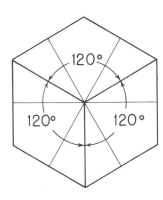

2. From each 120-degree corner, draw lines to the midpoint of the opposite sides.

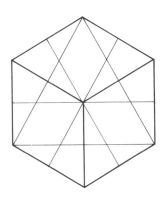

3. Using a 30-60 degree triangle do the same from the corners opposite the 120-degree corners.

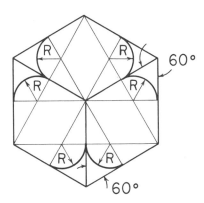

4. The intersection of these lines gives the center and the radius of each small circular arc near a 60-degree angle.

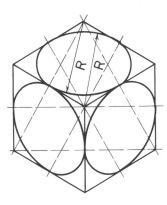

5. Use each 120-degree vertex as a center and the midpoint lines as a radii to complete each isometric circle.

PROBLEM

Make an isometric drawing of the objects shown on the facing page.

Scale: full size.

INSTRUCTIONS

1. Draw border lines and title block.

2. Draw light vertical and horizontal construction lines locating the four arc centers of each ellipse.

3. Use the step-by-step method of construction.

4. Omit dimension and hidden lines.

5. Use one sheet for each drawing.

6. Do not erase construction lines.

7. Omit dimensioning and hidden lines.

Drawing Isometric Circles in Different Planes

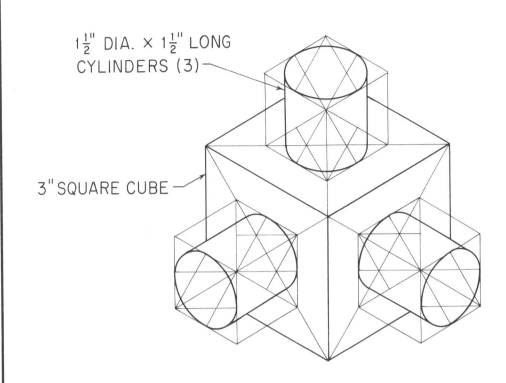

$1\frac{1}{2}$" DIA. × $1\frac{1}{2}$" LONG CYLINDERS (3)

3" SQUARE CUBE

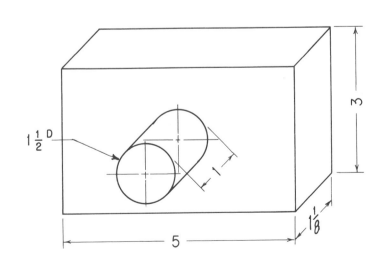

$1\frac{1}{2}$ D

1

3

5

$1\frac{1}{8}$

INFORMATION

A circular arc will appear in pictorial representation as a segment of an ellipse. Therefore, it may be drawn by using as much of the four-center method as is required to locate the needed centers. For example, to draw a quarter circle, it is only necessary to lay off the true radius of the arc along each of the two isometric lines, representing the two edges of an object, from their point of intersection. From these points intersecting perpendiculars are drawn to locate the center of the circular arc.

PROBLEM

Draw rounded ends and corners of the object shown on the following page in isometric projection.

Scale: full size.

Omit dimensions and hidden lines.

INSTRUCTIONS

1. Draw border lines and title block.

2. Center the isometric drawing of the object in a vertical position on the sheet.

3. Do not erase construction lines.

Drawing Arcs in Isometric Projection

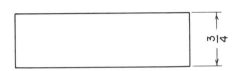

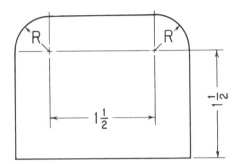

Given: Top and front views.

R = 1/2

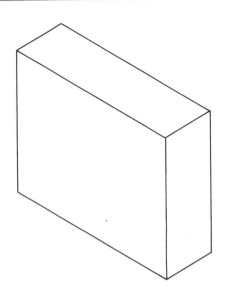

1. Draw object in isometric projection without round corners.

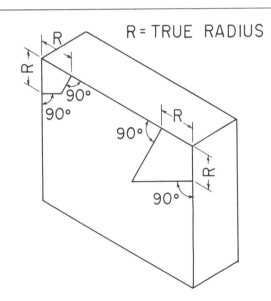

R = TRUE RADIUS

2. To draw a quarter circle for a round corner, it is only necessary to mark off the true radius of the arc *R*, along the isometric lines representing the edges of the object and draw intersecting perpendiculars from the ends of those marked-off lengths to determine the center of the circular arc.

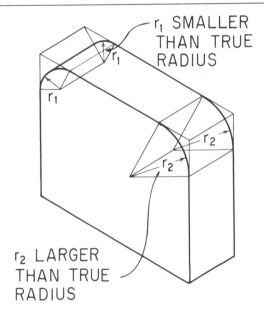

r_1 SMALLER THAN TRUE RADIUS

r_2 LARGER THAN TRUE RADIUS

3. Draw the arcs on the front face of the object. Repeat the procedure for drawing the arcs on the rear face of the object. Darken object lines to form object. Note that because of the isometric projection the arcs' radii may be larger or smaller than the true radius, as indicated.

INFORMATION

The figures on the facing page show various rounded ends and corners. Each is drawn in the same way as explained on page 227. Note that the contour element joining the two arcs, which is the visible edge of each rounded corner (see upper and lower left-hand figures), is drawn tangent to the two arcs.

PROBLEM

Draw portions of isometric circles to denote rounded ends and corners.

INSTRUCTIONS

1. Draw borderlines and title block.

2. Divide sheet into four equal parts.

3. Copy rounded corners and ends as shown in the four figures on page 228.

4. Measure each figure for dimensions and draw full size.

5. Use a 4H pencil for construction lines and an H pencil for object lines.

6. Darken portions of isometric circles.

7. Do not erase construction lines.

Drawing Isometric Rounded Corners and Ends

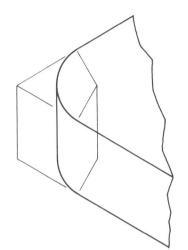

ROUNDED CORNER

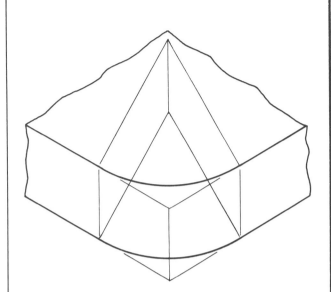

ROUNDED CORNER

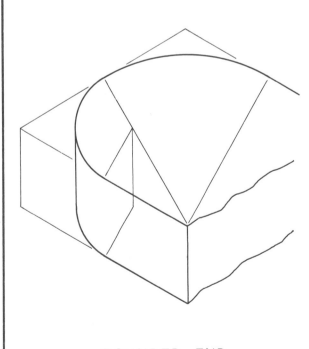

ROUNDED END

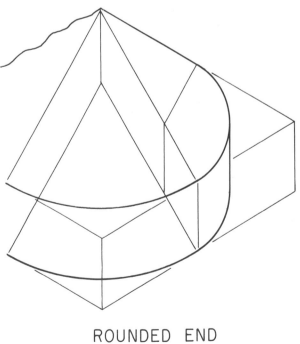

ROUNDED END

PROBLEM

Make isometric drawings of the angle brackets shown on the facing page.

Scale: full size.

INSTRUCTIONS

1. Draw border lines and title block.

2. Apply what you have learned in the previous lesson on Arcs in Isometric Projection to make isometric drawings of the objects shown.

3. Use a different sheet for each job.

4. Erase construction lines upon completion.

Practice in Drawing Isometric Circles and Arcs—1

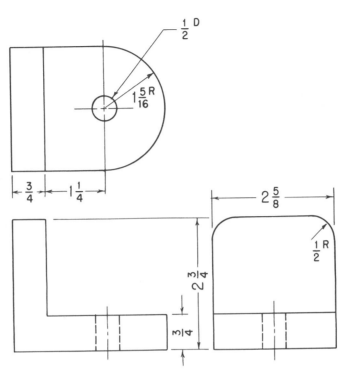

ANGLE BRACKET

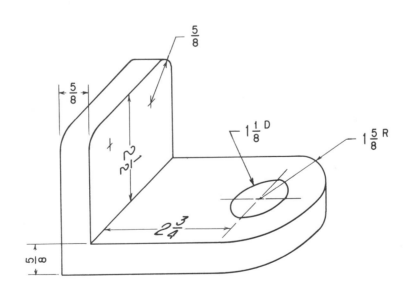

ANGLE BRACKET

INFORMATION

Although detail or working drawings provide all of the necessary working information and are best for showing a part when it is complicated or irregular, the draftsman may use a pictorial drawing as a means of presenting his ideas more simply, especially to a workman who lacks technical training. Such drawings present the objects approximately as they appear to the eye.

PROBLEM

Make an isometric drawing of objects shown on pages 233, 234 and 235.

Scale: full size.

INSTRUCTIONS

1. Draw border lines and title block.

2. Make isometric drawings of objects shown.

3. First draw the isometric square or cube.

4. Then draw circles and darken object lines.

5. Use a separate sheet of paper for each drawing.

6. Erase construction lines upon completion.

7. Omit dimensions, hidden lines and center lines.

Practice in Drawing Isometric Circles—2

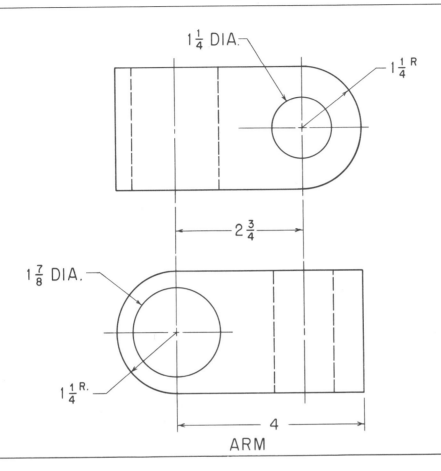

ARM

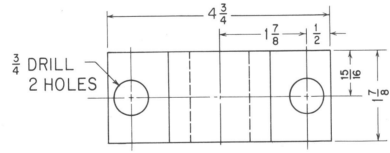

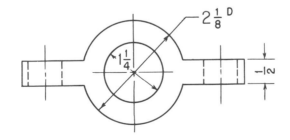

HOLDER

Practice in Drawing Isometric Circles and Arcs—3

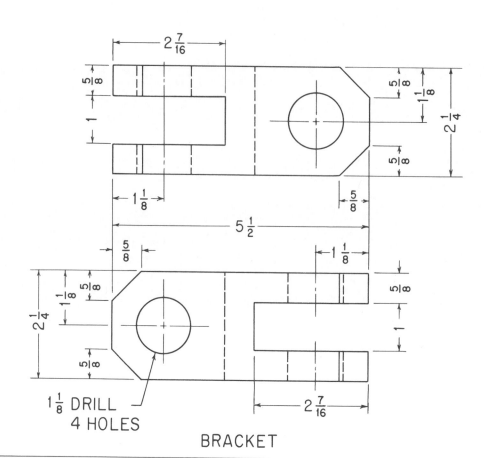

$1\frac{1}{8}$ DRILL
4 HOLES

BRACKET

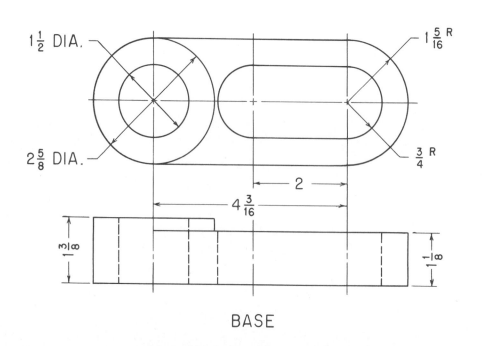

$1\frac{1}{2}$ DIA.

$2\frac{5}{8}$ DIA.

$1\frac{5}{16}$ R

$\frac{3}{4}$ R

BASE

Practice in Drawing Isometric Circles and Arcs—4

$\frac{3}{8}$ DRILL, $\frac{3}{4}$ C'BORE, $\frac{5}{16}$ DEEP - 3 HOLES

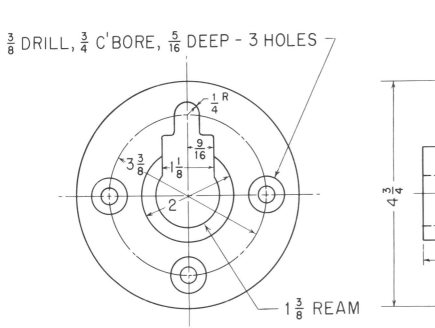

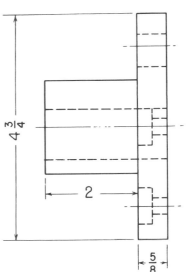

FLANGE

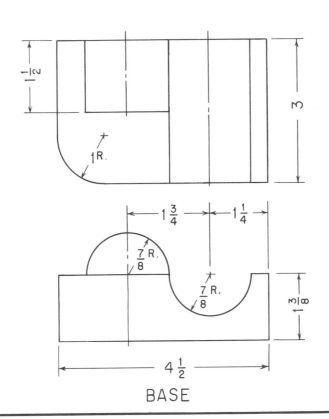

BASE

INFORMATION

In making an isometric drawing of the lever shown on the facing page, the box construction method is used. As shown, two rectangular boxes with square holes are drawn at the given center distance to represent the two cylindrical ends of the lever. The two boxes are joined by light construction lines which actually do no more than indicate that the two boxes are part of one unit.

Note that the bottom plane of the joining web, although horizontal, does not coincide with the plane in which the bases of the two cylindrical ends lie. Also the slanting vertical part of the web extends only a small distance either side of the horizontal center line. Note that the front edges of the web connecting the two cylindrical ends must be drawn as non-isometric lines.

The four-center method of constructing approximate ellipses shown in this unit is generally used because it is relatively easy and saves time.

PROBLEM

Make an isometric drawing of object shown.

Scale: full size.

INSTRUCTIONS

1. Draw border lines and title block.

2. Lay out all construction lines with a 4H pencil.

3. Darken all object lines with an H pencil.

4. Erase construction lines upon completion.

5. Omit dimensions, hidden lines and center lines.

Practice in Isometric Drawing

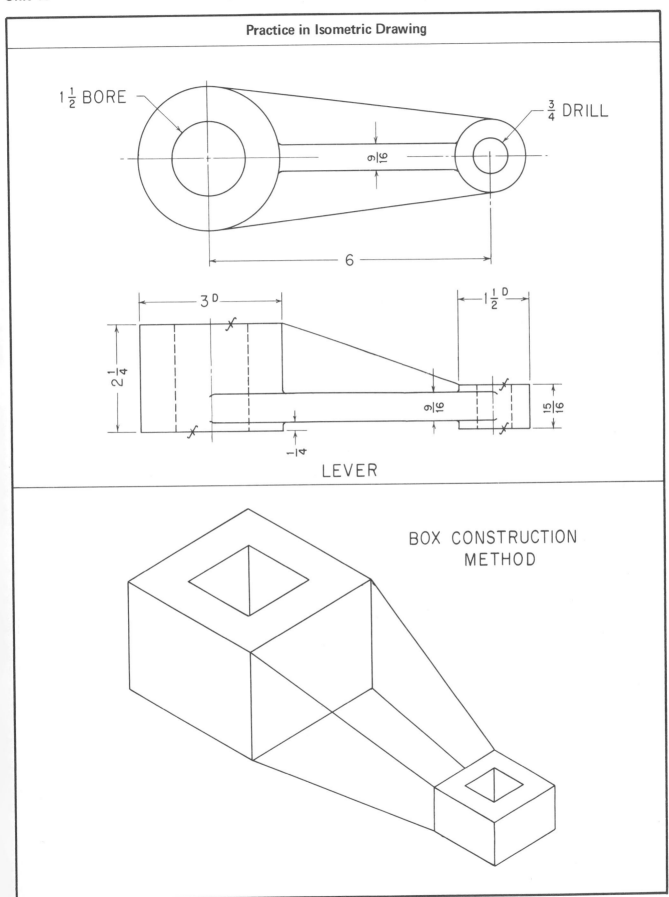

$1\frac{1}{2}$ BORE

$\frac{3}{4}$ DRILL

$\frac{9}{16}$

6

3^{D}

$1\frac{1}{2}^{D}$

$2\frac{1}{4}$

$\frac{9}{16}$

$\frac{15}{16}$

$\frac{1}{4}$

LEVER

BOX CONSTRUCTION
METHOD

Review Questions

Unit 19 review questions to be answered on a separate sheet of paper.

DIRECTIONS

For each of the numbered statements below, write the number and after it the figure, symbol, word or words which will complete the sentence. Do NOT write in the book.

1. Construct an isometric cube with the diameter of the _____ needed as the length of an edge.
   a) square
   b) triangle
   c) circle
   d) cube
   e) rectangle

2. Use the _____ degree vertex as a center and the mid-point line as a radius to complete an isometric circle.
   a) 30
   b) 120
   c) 60
   d) 90
   e) 125

3. Draw the isometric circle by the _____ point center system.
   a) one
   b) four
   c) three
   d) five
   e) two

4. Artistic skill is necessary in _____ drawing.
   a) orthographic
   b) photo
   c) pictorial
   d) auxiliary
   e) section

5. Circles and arcs in isometric drawings will appear as _____.
   a) squares
   b) ellipses
   c) rectangles
   d) triangles
   e) circles

6. To draw the isometric view of a circle, first draw the circumscribing isometric _____.
   a) curve
   b) triangle
   c) square
   d) ellipse
   e) center

7. The draftsman's triangle used to make an isometric circle is _____ degrees.
   a) 45
   b) 30 - 60
   c) 15
   d) 90
   e) 115

8. The isometric circle is similar to a/an _____.
   a) circumference
   b) curve
   c) chord
   d) oblique
   e) ellipse

9. A draftsman may use a/an _____ drawing as a means of presenting his ideas more simply.
   a) orthographic
   b) pictorial
   c) working
   d) true view
   e) detail

10. An isometric projection presents an object approximately as it appears to the _____.
    a) airplane
    b) microscope
    c) enlarger
    d) reducer
    e) eye

NOTES AND DIMENSIONS- WORKING DRAWINGS

The purpose of this unit is to explain how to make a working drawing.

Up to now we have learned how to draw in orthographic projection. Now we will introduce dimensioning and specifications.

A detail drawing, in addition to showing the shape of a part, must furnish the workman with information on the distances between surfaces, locations of holes, kinds of finish, types of materials, number required etc. The placing of this information on a drawing by the use of lines, symbols, figures and notes is known as dimensioning.

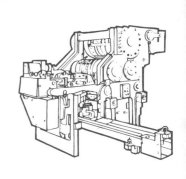

INFORMATION

Many small parts or details are used in the construction of mechanical devices, even when the design is not particularly complex. The draftsman should know how to represent these details clearly using methods which avoid useless and tedious work.

He should not only be familiar with the different machine details and conventional methods in general use, but he should also understand how and where to employ them.

As will be explained, a generally recognized system of lines, symbols, figures and notes is used to indicate size and location.

PROBLEM

Draw each figure illustrating a machining term and letter the dimensioning notes, as shown on the following page.

INSTRUCTIONS

1. Draw border lines and title block.

2. Divide paper into six equal parts.

3. In each part draw the illustration and letter the dimensioning notes.

4. All lettering is to be 1/8 inch high.

Terms and Notes Used on Working Drawings—1

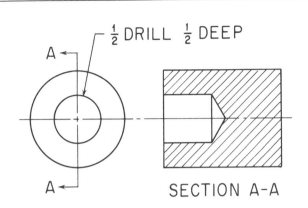

1. DRILL—To sink a hole with a drill.

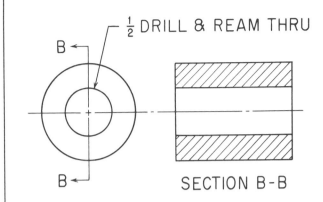

2. REAM—To enlarge or finish a drilled hole with a reamer.

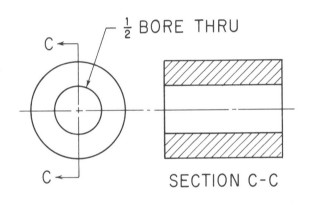

3. BORE—To make or enlarge a hole with a boring tool.

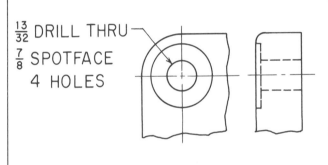

4. SPOTFACE—To finish a round spot on a rough surface.

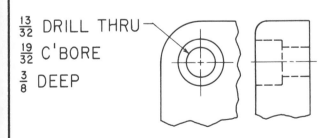

5. COUNTERBORE—To enlarge a hole to a given depth.

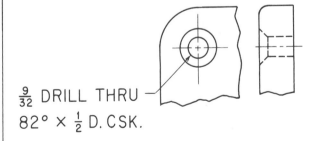

6. COUNTERSINK—To form a depression to fit the conical head of a screw.

INFORMATION

Leaders are thin lines beginning with a short horizontal line segment at the note, callout, or dimension and terminating in an arrowhead at the point of application. They are used to indicate the features to which the callouts, notes, or dimensions apply. See illustrations on facing page.

Leaders will preferably be drawn at an angle of 15 degrees minimum to the vertical or horizontal axes of the drawing. If adjacent extension and dimension lines are also drawn at an angle, the leaders will be drawn at a different angle. The arrowhead should terminate exactly on the line which represents the outline of the feature.

PROBLEM

Illustrate machining and machine terms and dimensioning notes, as shown in this group.

INSTRUCTIONS

1. Draw border lines and title block.

2. Divide paper into six equal parts.

3. In each part draw illustration and its corresponding dimensioning notes.

4. All lettering is to be 1/8 inch high.

5. Scale original drawing to obtain dimensions.

Terms and Notes Used on Working Drawings—2	
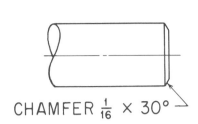 CHAMFER $\frac{1}{16}$ × 30°	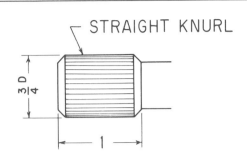 STRAIGHT KNURL
7. CHAMFER—To bevel a sharp external edge.	8. KNURL—To roughen or indent a turned surface.
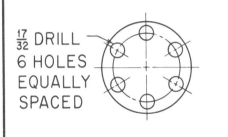 $\frac{17}{32}$ DRILL 6 HOLES EQUALLY SPACED	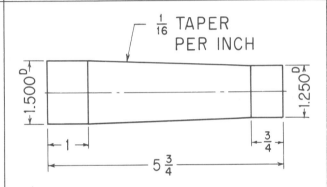 $\frac{1}{16}$ TAPER PER INCH
9. DRILLED HOLES—In dimensioning drilled holes indicate by note as shown above.	10. TAPER—The taper of a piece is the difference between the large diameter and the small diameter over a given length. It is often expressed as so much difference in diameter, per inch in length or per foot in length.
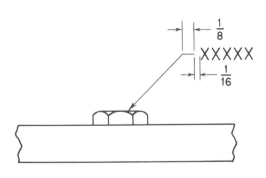	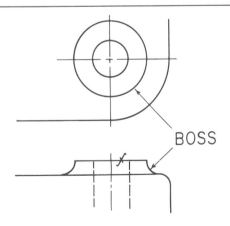 BOSS
11. LEADER—A leader is a thin line with an arrowhead pointing to and in contact with some feature on the drawing.	12. BOSS—A boss is a raised portion or pad on a flat surface often circular and located around a hole.

INFORMATION

After a drawing of a part has been completely dimensioned, it is still not a working drawing, for although the workman using it would know the exact shape and size, many other things must be known before actual construction or manufacture can begin. Such information cannot be shown by projections and must therefore be given in the form of notes.

PROBLEM

Illustrate machine terms and dimensioning notes, as shown in this group.

INSTRUCTIONS

1. Draw border lines and title block.
2. Divide paper into six equal parts.
3. In each part draw machine terms and their corresponding dimensioning notes.
4. All lettering to be 1/8 inch high.
5. Scale original drawing for dimensions.

Terms and Notes Used on Working Drawings—3

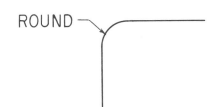

13. ROUND—A round is put on the outside of a piece to improve appearance, and to avoid forming a sharp edge that might chip off under a sharp blow.

14. FILLET—A fillet is additional metal allowed in the inner intersection of two surfaces to increase the strength of the object.

15. DIAMOND KNURLING—This is represented by a series of cross lines on the surfaces being knurled.

NECK $\frac{1}{16}$ WIDE $\frac{1}{32}$ DEEP

16. NECKING—The operation of necking is indicated by a note.

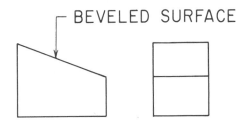

17. BEVELED SURFACE—A beveled surface is a cut on the entire length or width of a piece at an angle to some horizontal or vertical plane.

18. PAD—A pad is a slight projection above the surface of an object.

INFORMATION

The surfaces of a rough casting or forging that are to be machined or "finished" are indicated with a finish mark or symbol. This symbol is placed in all views on the visible and invisible edge lines of the surfaces to be machined.

Parts which are to have an ordinary machine finish on all surfaces should be marked FAO or with a note "FINISH ALL OVER."

When the amount of allowable surface roughness is to be specified, a surface roughness symbol is used. This is a V-shape or check mark usually with one heavy leg of "flag" at the top of which may be placed a short horizontal line.

The following terms are used in describing surface finish or texture:

1. WAVINESS—Large irregularities in the surface.

2. ROUGHNESS—Closely spaced peaks and valleys found on any surface.

3. LAY—The direction of the tool marks and scratches produced in finishing the surface.

The above is intended only as an introduction to the subject of surface symbols.

PROBLEM

Copy the symbols on the facing page.

INSTRUCTIONS

Use a soft H pencil with a triangle to copy the symbols. Note carefully angles and proportions where indicated.

Surface Finish and Roughness Symbols

A finish mark indicates that a surface is to be machined.

The finish mark is shown on the edge views of the surface to be machined, and should be repeated on all edge views of that surface.

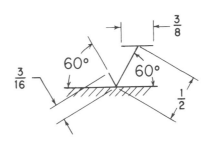

1. Formerly, an italic *f* was used to indicate a surface to be finished.

2. A surface to be machined or "finished" from an unfinished material such as a casting or forging should be marked with a 60-degree V.

3. Surface roughness symbol—recommended proportions.

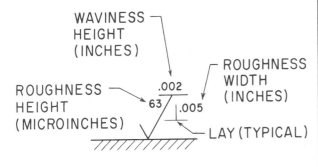

WAVINESS HEIGHT (INCHES)

ROUGHNESS WIDTH (INCHES)

ROUGHNESS HEIGHT (MICROINCHES)

.002

63

.005

LAY (TYPICAL)

4. The maximum roughness height in microinches is placed to the left of the long leg. A second or minimum value is sometimes shown directly underneath the first. Figures for maximum allowable waviness height and roughness width are placed around the V symbol as shown. One of several lay symbols may also be used.

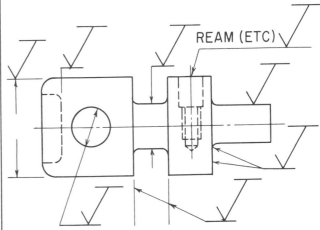

REAM (ETC)

5. When space is limited, or when there is an alignment problem, leaders or extension lines may be used to direct application of the symbol to a machined surface.

INFORMATION

.3125 DRILL

A hole which is to be produced by drilling should have the diameter given, followed by the word indicating the operation, and, if more than one, the number of the same size holes to be drilled. A leader is drawn from the note to the circle representing the hole, and in line with center of the hole.

Notes for holes made with drills one-half inch in diameter and smaller should be written as decimal fractions. The drills selected in this range should be the standard diameters given in the USASI Standard for Straight Shank Twist Drills USAS B94.11. The indication of the diameters of drills larger than one-half inch should be expressed in units and decimals. If common fractions are employed, the decimal equivalent should be given.

The table on the facing page gives the diameters in decimal inches of number and letter size drills. In addition to these sizes, twist drills run from 1/64-inch diameter to 1¼-inch diameter by sixty-fourths; from 1¼-inch diameter to 1½-inch diameter by thirty-seconds and from 1½-inch diameter to 2-inch diameter by sixteenths of an inch.

Number and Letter Size Twist Drills

NUMBER SIZES

No.	Dia.	No.	Dia.	No.	Dia.	No.	Dia.
1	.2280	25	.1495	49	.0730	73	.0240
2	.2210	26	.1470	50	.0700	74	.0225
3	.2130	27	.1440	51	.0670	75	.0210
4	.2090	28	.1405	52	.0635	76	.0200
5	.2055	29	.1360	53	.0595	77	.0180
6	.2040	30	.1285	54	.0550	78	.0160
7	.2010	31	.1200	55	.0520	79	.0145
8	.1990	32	.1160	56	.0465	80	.0135
9	.1960	33	.1130	57	.0430	81	.0130
10	.1935	34	.1110	58	.0420	82	.0125
11	.1910	35	.1100	59	.0410	83	.0120
12	.1890	36	.1065	60	.0400	84	.0115
13	.1850	37	.1040	61	.0390	85	.0110
14	.1820	38	.1015	62	.0380	86	.0105
15	.1800	39	.0995	63	.0370	87	.0100
16	.1770	40	.0980	64	.0360	88	.0095
17	.1730	41	.0960	65	.0350	89	.0091
18	.1695	42	.0935	66	.0330	90	.0087
19	.1660	43	.0890	67	.0320	91	.0083
20	.1610	44	.0860	68	.0310	92	.0079
21	.1590	45	.0820	69	.0292	93	.0075
22	.1570	46	.0810	70	.0280	94	.0071
23	.1540	47	.0785	71	.0260	95	.0067
24	.1520	48	.0760	72	.0250	96	.0063

LETTER SIZES

Let.	Dia.	Let.	Dia.	Let.	Dia.	Let.	Dia.
A	.2340	H	.2660	O	.3160	V	.3770
B	.2380	I	.2720	P	.3230	W	.3860
C	.2420	J	.2770	Q	.3320	X	.3970
D	.2460	K	.2810	R	.3390	Y	.4040
E	.2500	L	.2900	S	.3480	Z	.4130
F	.2570	M	.2950	T	.3580		
G	.2610	N	.3020	U	.3680		

Review Questions

Unit 20 review questions to be answered on a separate sheet of paper.

DIRECTIONS:

For each of the numbered statements below, write the number and after it the figure, symbol, word or words which will complete the sentence. Do NOT write in the book.

1. To finish a drilled hole you would ____.
   a) spotface
   b) bore
   c) ream
   d) counterbore
   e) countersink

2. To enlarge a hole with a boring tool, you would ____.
   a) knurl
   b) bore
   c) countersink
   d) drill
   e) counterbore

3. To finish a round spot on a rough surface you would ____.
   a) spotface
   b) boss
   c) pad
   d) taper
   e) chamfer

4. To enlarge a hole to a given depth you would ____.
   a) drill
   b) counterbore
   c) section
   d) bevel
   e) fillet

5. To form a depression to fit the conical head of a screw you would ____.
   a) pad
   b) finish
   c) countersink
   d) boss
   e) fillet

6. A finish mark indicates that a surface is to be _____.
   a) sectioned
   b) machined
   c) knurled
   d) tapered
   e) bisected

7. To roughen or indent a turned surface you would _____.
   a) finish
   b) bevel
   c) knurl
   d) taper
   e) chamfer

8. To bevel a sharp external edge you would _____.
   a) taper
   b) boss
   c) chamfer
   d) knurl
   e) machine

9. A round is put on the _____ of an object.
   a) outside
   b) middle
   c) inside
   d) left
   e) right

10. A fillet is additional metal allowed in the _____ of two surfaces.
   a) outside
   b) intersection
   c) bevel
   d) taper
   e) machining

INFORMATION

Size dimensions—Size dimensions give the size of a piece, component part, hole, or slot.

Location dimensions—Location dimensions fix the relationship of the component parts (projections, holes, slots, and other significant forms) of a piece or structure. Particular care must be exercised in their selection and placement, because upon them depend the accuracy of the operations in making a piece and the proper mating of the piece with other parts.

Placing dimensions—Dimensions should be placed where they will be most easily understood—in the locations where the shop man will expect to find them.

PROBLEM

Draw border lines and title block. Make a three-view orthographic drawing of each part shown on pages 255 to 258. Include dimensions and notes. Note that arrow labeled F indicates direction of sight for front view.

INSTRUCTIONS

1. Draw full size front and top views of the objects shown.

2. Allow 1 inch between views.

3. Show hidden lines and center lines.

4. Before starting these problems, study the pictorial drawings given and see just what is required in each case. See how the object is to be represented and the best method of showing it. It will be necessary to use judgment to arrange for spacing of views for the detail drawings of each piece.

5. Each object should be completely dimensioned and should be identified.

6. Use a different sheet for each job.

Practice in Making Working Drawings—1

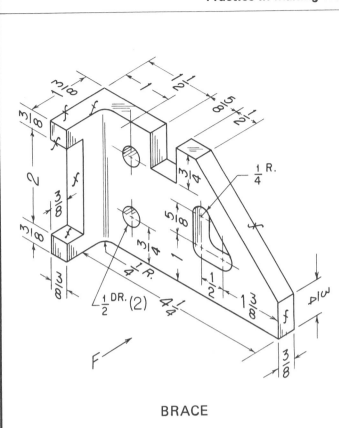

BRACE

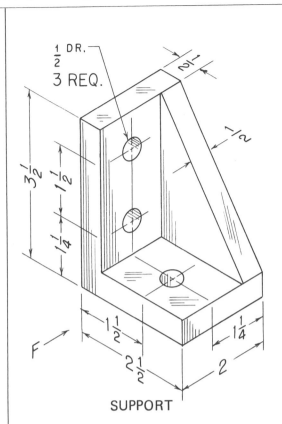

SUPPORT

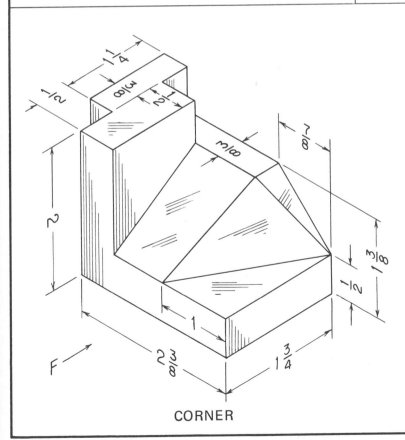

CORNER

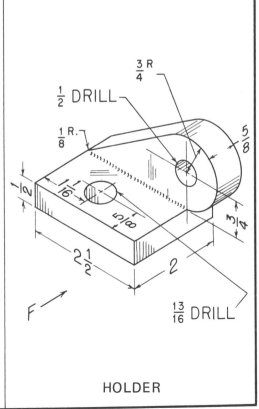

HOLDER

Practice in Making Working Drawings—2

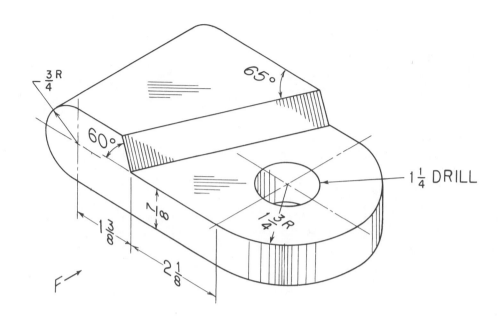

1.

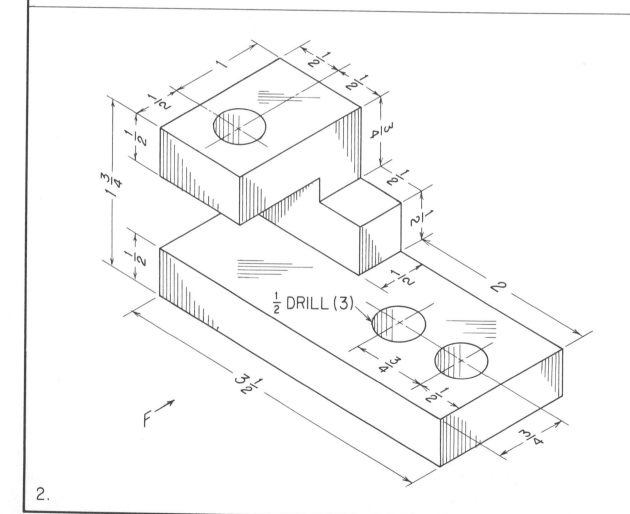

2.

Practice in Making Working Drawings—3

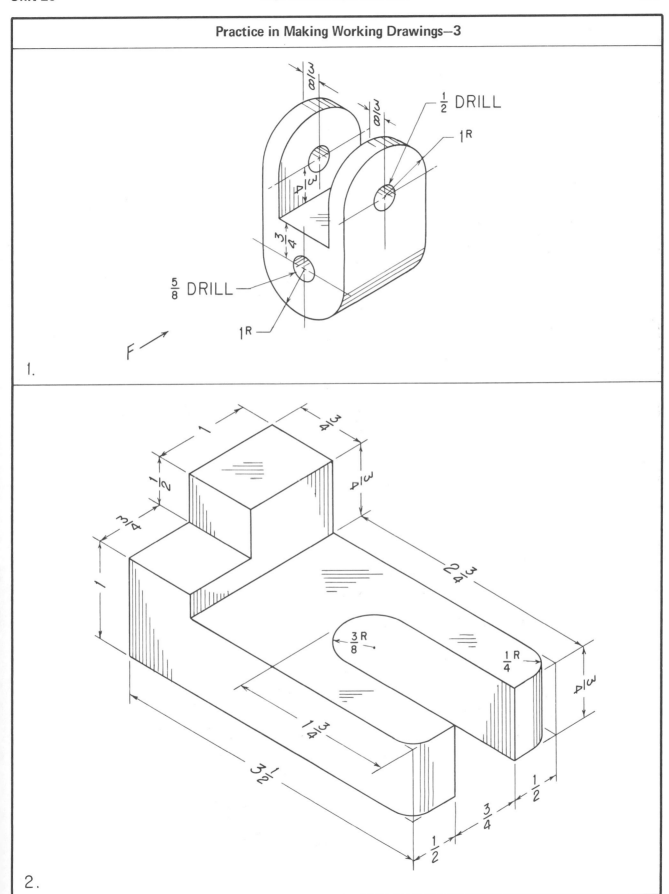

1.

2.

Practice in Making Working Drawings—4

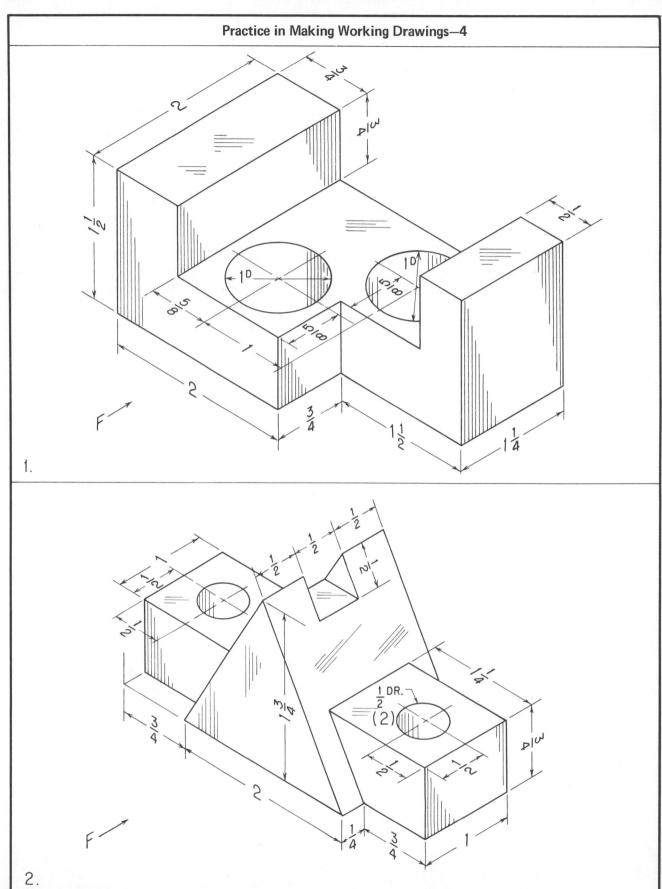

1.

2.

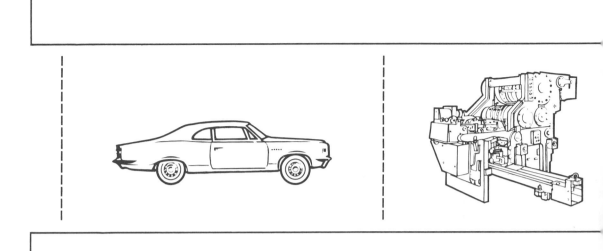

UNIT 21

AUXILIARY VIEWS

The purpose of this unit is to show how to draw
auxiliary views and how to find the true lengths
of lines and the true shapes of objects.

INFORMATION

Up to this point, the drawings discussed have consisted of only 1-, 2- or 3-view working drawings. However, many objects have slanting surfaces or other features which cannot be shown in their true size and shape in the conventional 3-view drawing. Consequently, auxiliary views are needed.

Three auxiliary views are shown on the facing page. Note that in each case the auxiliary view is projected at right angles to the slanting surface which it represents. In the upper righthand illustration the auxiliary view is projected from the slanting surface in the front view, hence, it is called a front auxiliary view. Similarly, the top auxiliary view is projected from the slanting surface in the top view and the side auxiliary view is projected from the slanting surface in the side view as shown by the two other illustrations on the facing page.

Referring to the figures on the facing page, in the front auxiliary view the width of the object is rotated from the top view until it is at right angles to the length in the auxiliary view. In the top auxiliary view the width is rotated from the front view until it is at right angles to the length in the auxiliary view. In the side auxiliary view the length is rotated until it is at right angles to the width in the auxiliary view.

PROBLEM

In your graph notebook make a freehand sketch of each of the three types of auxiliary views as shown on the following page. In each case label the auxiliary view and the two regular views.

The Three Auxiliary Views

These three auxiliary views show how each is projected from two regular views. Thus, the front auxiliary view is shown projected from the front and top views. The top auxiliary view is shown projected from the top and front views. The side auxiliary view is shown projected from the side and front views. Note that a different object is shown in each illustration.

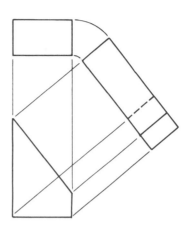

1. Front auxiliary, projected from front view.

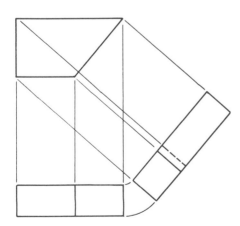

2. Top auxiliary, projected from top view.

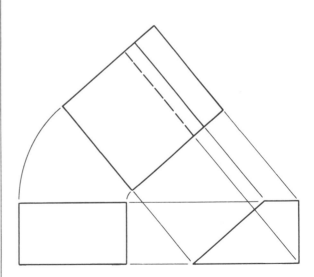

3. Side auxiliary, projected from side view.

INFORMATION

Objects having *slanting* surfaces cannot possibly be shown in true shape or size by the conventional front, top, or side views. The only way in which the true size or shape of the sloping surface can be shown is by projecting lines at right angles (90°) to the surface, and drawing an auxiliary view as shown on the facing page.

An auxiliary view is an orthographic projection on a plane perpendicular to one of the principal planes of projection but inclined to the other two.

PROBLEM

Draw auxiliary views of the geometrical figures shown on pages 264 to 267.

INSTRUCTIONS

1. Draw the required auxiliary views, showing the complete object in each problem.

2. Use a 4H pencil for construction lines, a 2H pencil for center lines and a sharp F pencil for object lines.

3. Letter the reference plane line in the auxiliary view, using guide lines.

4. Show the true size and shape of the inclined surface.

5. Follow the step-by-step method to make the drawings.

Projecting the Auxiliary View

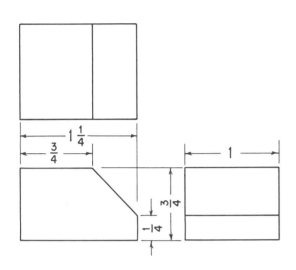

1. The three regular views.

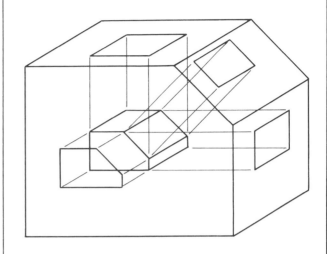

2. The projection box.

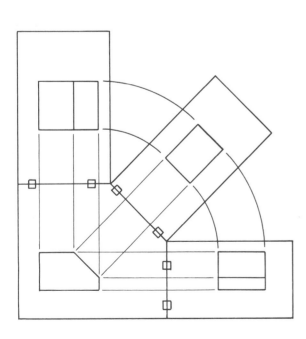

3. The projection box with sides swung out and laid flat.

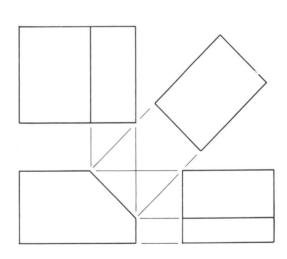

4. The three regular views with the front auxiliary view added.

Drawing Auxiliary View of Truncated Triangular Prism

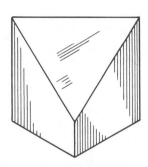

TRUNCATED TRIANGULAR
PRISM

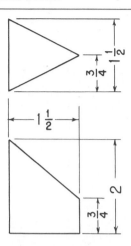

1. Draw the front and top views to the dimensions shown.

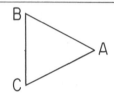

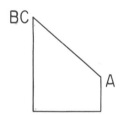

2. Label corners of front and top views.

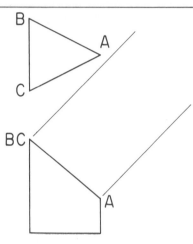

3. Project construction lines from BC and A in front view.

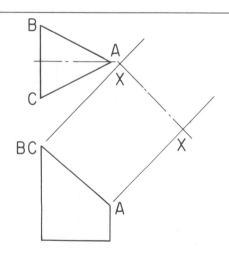

4. Construct center line X-X parallel to line BC-A.

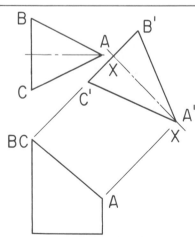

5. Measure true width B-C. Lay it out as B'-C' across center line X'-X'. Complete the auxiliary view.

Drawing Auxiliary View of Truncated Hexagonal Prism

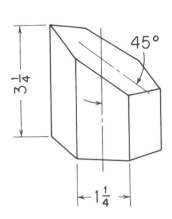

TRUNCATED HEXAGONAL PRISM

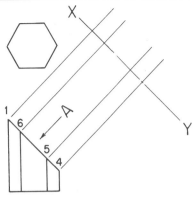

1. Draw construction lines from points 1, 6, 5, & 4 in front view perpendicular to surface A. Draw center line XY at right angles to these lines and parallel with surface A.

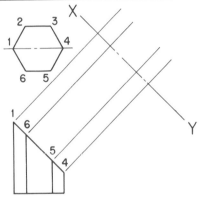

2. Label corners of top view corresponding to those in front view and draw a center line through points 1 and 4.

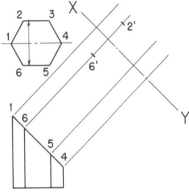

3. Set one leg of the dividers on point 2 of top view and take off the distance to point 6. Transfer this distance to construction line 6 as shown at 2'-6' across center line X-Y.

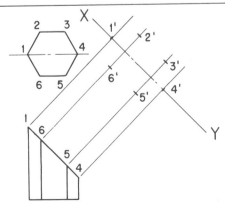

4. Since distance 2-6 in top view is equal to distance 3-5, the same setting of the dividers as in step 3 is used in laying off 3'-5' on construction line 5 in the auxiliary view.

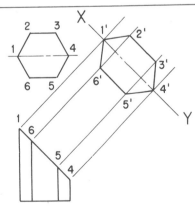

5. Connect points 1', 2', 3', 4', 5', 6' and 1' with straight lines thus forming the auxiliary view.

Drawing Auxiliary View of a Truncated Cylinder

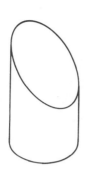

TRUNCATED CYLINDER

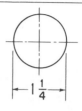

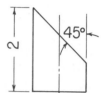

1. Draw the top and front views.

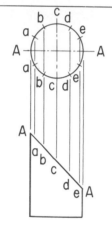

2. Divide the top view into 12 equal parts and project the divisions to the front view.

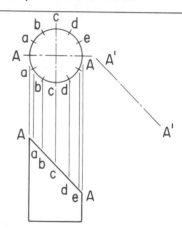

3. Draw a center line A'-A' for the auxiliary view parallel to the inclined face at any convenient distance from the face.

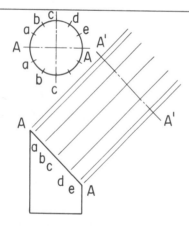

4. Project the necessary construction lines from the slanted edge through center line A'-A'. the projected lines are at right angles (90°) to the inclined face.

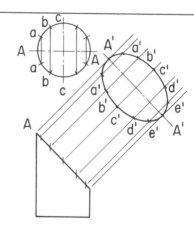

5. With dividers take measurements from the top view (a-a, b-b, c-c) and transfer one-half to the right and one-half to the left of center line A'-A'. Complete the auxiliary view by connecting the points with a French curve.

Further Practice with Auxiliary Views

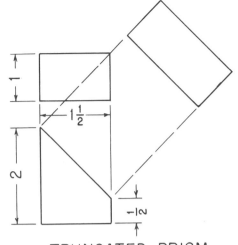

TRUNCATED PRISM

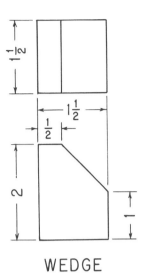

WEDGE

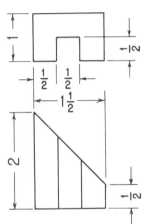

TRUNCATED CHANNEL

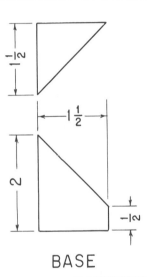

BASE

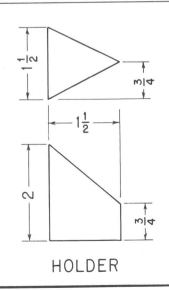

HOLDER

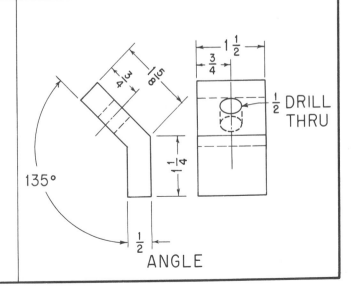

ANGLE

INFORMATION

Certain kinds of lines and plane faces on some objects do not show in their true length or shape in the three principal views. In construction, however, it is frequently necessary to know three things about lines and planes as follows:

1. The true length of inclined lines.

2. The angle between lines.

3. The true shape of plane faces.

The first two or these items can be obtained by finding the third.

PROBLEM

Make a working drawing of objects shown on the facing page. Include an auxiliary view.

INSTRUCTIONS

1. Draw border lines and title block.

2. With a 4H pencil draw construction lines.

3. With an H pencil draw all object lines.

4. Label top, front, and auxiliary views.

5. Make the drawing of each object on a separate sheet.

Drawing Front Auxiliary Views

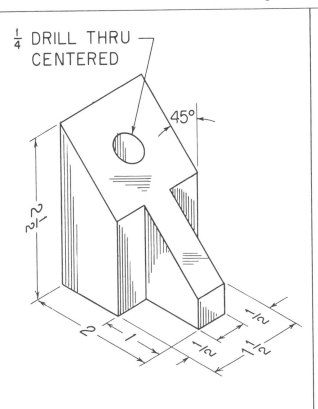

¼ DRILL THRU
CENTERED

45°

2½

2

1

½

½

1½

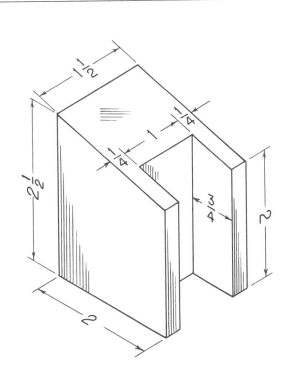

1½

¼

1

¼

2½

¾

2

2

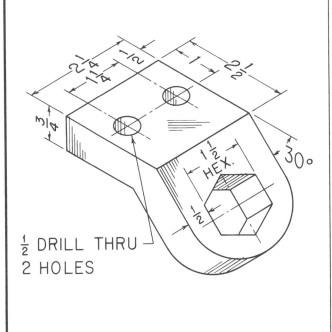

2½

1¼

½

1

2½

¾

1½
HEX.

30°

½

½ DRILL THRU
2 HOLES

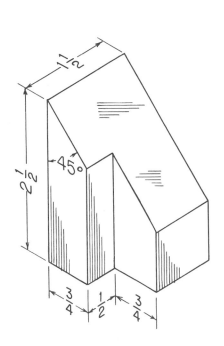

1½

45°

2½

¾

½

¾

INFORMATION

Often the use of an auxiliary view allows one of the principal views (front, top, or side) to be eliminated. In another method of simplification, a partial auxiliary view is shown. For example, a feature such as a slot or square opening may be symmetrical in both size and position so that only part of it need be shown. Several holes may be of the same size and symmetrically located so that only enough need be shown to indicate the position of the remainder. Thus, the shape description furnished by the partial view is, together with the regular views shown, sufficient for a complete understanding of the shape of the part and its features. The use of partial views simplifies the drawing, saves valuable drafting time, and often tends to make the drawing easier to read.

In making a partial view an irregular line is used at a convenient location to indicate the imaginary break.

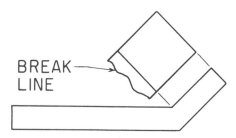

PROBLEM

Make a working drawing of each of the objects shown on pages 271 to 273. Include a partial auxiliary view for each. Note, however, that the clip shown in the last drawing at the bottom of page 273 has two different slanting surfaces and hence will require a separate auxiliary view for each or, in other words, a left front auxiliary view and a right front auxiliary view.

INSTRUCTIONS

1. Draw border lines and title block.

2. Use one sheet for the drawing of each object.

3. Dimension fully.

Drawing Partial Auxiliary Views—1

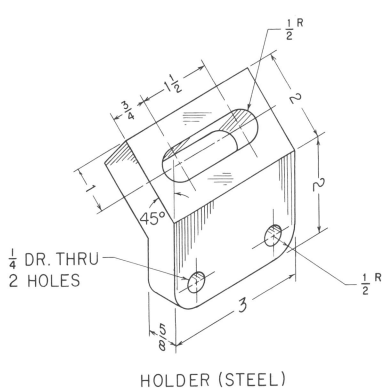

HOLDER (STEEL)

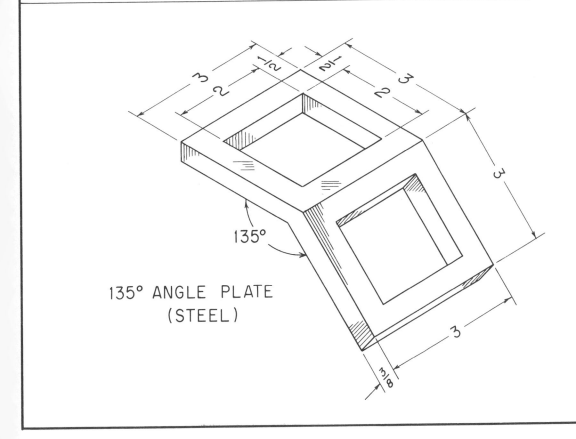

135° ANGLE PLATE
(STEEL)

Drawing Partial Auxiliary Views—2

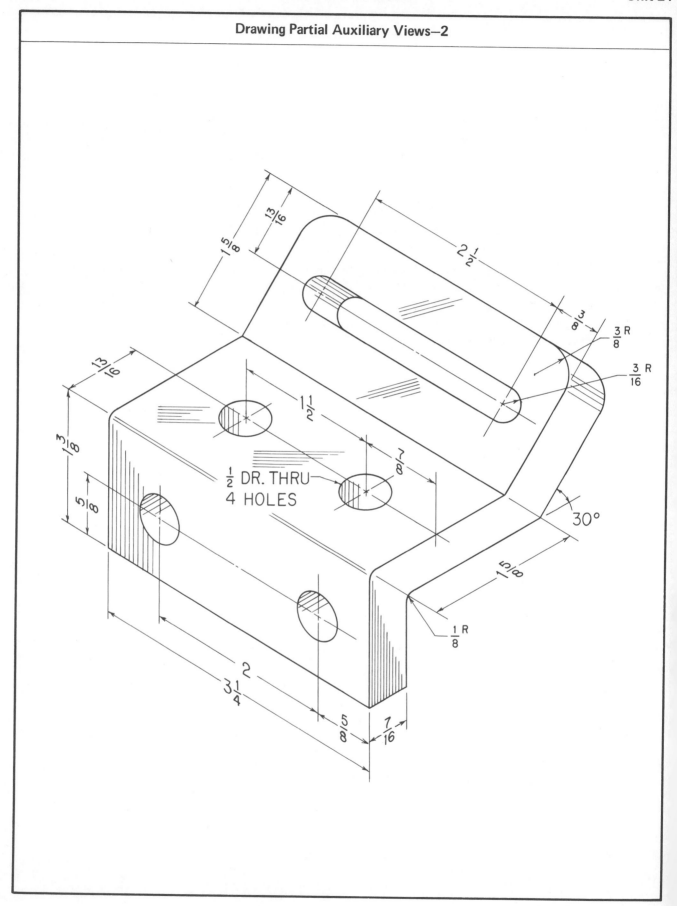

Drawing Partial Auxiliary Views—3

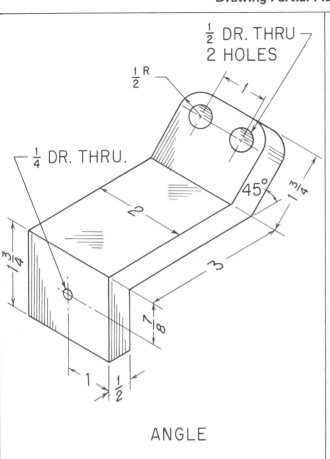

ANGLE

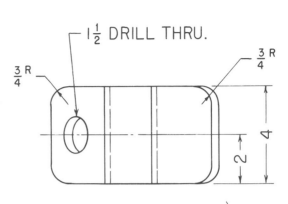

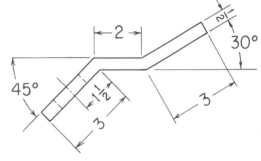

BRACKET

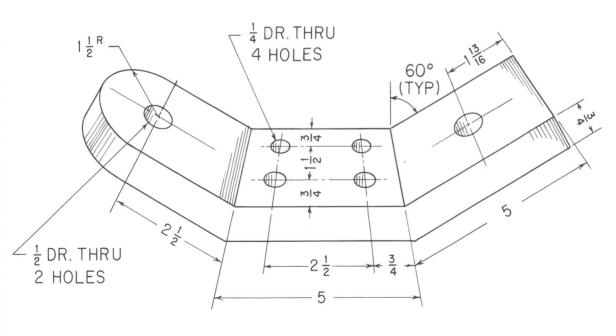

CLIP

Review Questions

Unit 21 review questions to be answered on a separate sheet of paper.

DIRECTIONS:
For each of the numbered statements below, write the number and after it the figure, symbol, word or words which will complete the sentence. Do NOT write in the book.

1. True sizes and shapes of slanted surfaces are obtained by projecting directly from the _____.
   a) right
   b) section
   c) counterbore
   d) slant
   e) finish

2. An auxiliary view is often shown as a part of a _____.
   a) section
   b) casting
   c) view
   d) forging
   e) perspective

3. The auxiliary view is obtained by projecting the _____ surface on a plane parallel to it.
   a) bottom
   b) left
   c) slanted
   d) middle
   e) right

4. The true shape of an object with slanted surfaces can only be represented by a/an _____ view.
   a) cavalier
   b) perspective
   c) auxiliary
   d) isometric
   e) oblique

5. An auxiliary view shows the true size and _____ of an object.
   a) color
   b) dimension
   c) shape
   d) section
   e) line

6. An auxiliary view is an orthographic projection on a plane perpendicular to one of the principal planes of projection but _____ to the other two.
   a) straight
   b) perpendicular
   c) inclined
   d) curved
   e) true

7. The usual views of an object do not show the true shapes of _____ surfaces.
   a) straight
   b) slanting
   c) isometric
   d) square
   e) triangular

8. The three regular planes are the top or horizontal plane, the front or frontal plane, and the side or _____ plane.
   a) auxiliary
   b) isometric
   c) square
   d) profile
   e) irregular

9. An auxiliary view is a projection on an auxiliary plane parallel to a _____ surface.
   a) regular
   b) square
   c) straight
   d) slanting
   e) triangular

10. Auxiliary views are important for describing shapes of _____ features.
   a) straight
   b) round
   c) inclined
   d) square
   e) angular

SCREW THREADS

The purpose of this unit is to present the principal facts concerning the standard thread forms and to show how to represent and note them on drawings.

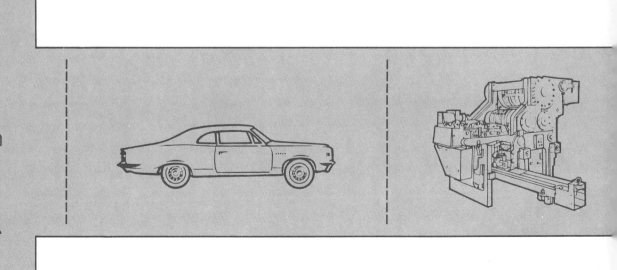

INFORMATION

A screw thread may be considered to be an inclined plane wrapped around a cylinder. The Egyptians used this principle to haul material for the building of their pyramids up long slopes wound around the pyramids.

A few centuries later this principle was used in building the Roman Circus. A helical roadway was built around the outer wall so that the chariots of the Roman Emperor and other notables could be driven to their places high in the structure.

Thus, when an inclined plane is wrapped around a cylinder, it forms a helix. The helix is defined as a curve made by a point which moves uniformly around a cylinder and at the same time advances uniformly lengthwise along the cylinder.

PROBLEM

Draw a helix around a cylinder and its horizontal development.

INSTRUCTIONS

1. Draw border lines and title block.

2. Follow the step-by-step procedure of constructing a helix shown on the facing page.

3. Draw a horizontal development of the helix.

4. Label and number all lines as shown in the figures on the facing page.

Constructing a Helix

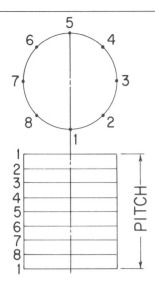

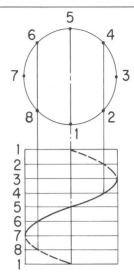

1. Draw top and front views of the cylinder.
2. Divide the top view into 8 equal parts and the pitch into the same number of parts as in top view.

3. From each point in the top view drop a perpendicular to meet the horizontal line drawn through the same numbered division of the front view.
4. A smooth curve drawn through the points found will give the projection of the helix.

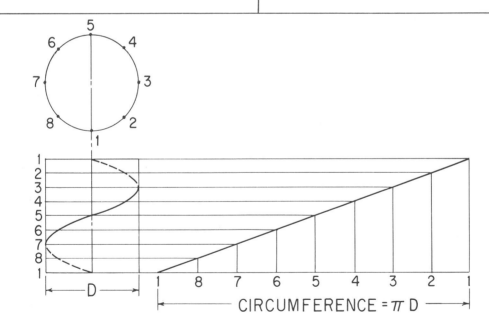

5. Draw a horizontal projection stretchout line equal in length to the circumference of the cylinder and divide it into 8 equal parts.
6. Each horizontal line of the cylinder is extended to meet the correspondingly numbered vertical line rising from the stretchout line. If this is done accurately, these points of intersection will all lie on an inclined straight line. This is what the helix would look like if it were unwound from the cylinder.

INFORMATION

Brief descriptions of different ways in which screw threads are cut or formed will be found on the facing page.

A large number of threaded fasteners are used in industry and the draftsman is frequently called upon to show these in his drawings. It is important, then, for him to become acquainted with the various forms of threads and how they are used. This will be explained in succeeding pages of this unit.

PROBLEM

To learn how screw threads are cut and formed.

INSTRUCTIONS

After reading the information on page 281, refer to any metalworking reference text or handbook for supplementary information on the cutting and forming of screw threads.

Cutting and Forming of Screw Threads

EXTERNAL AND INTERNAL THREADS
     There are both outside (external) and inside (internal) threads. The outside threads are those on a machine screw or on a bolt. The inside threads are those cut inside a nut or hole.

HOW EXTERNAL THREADS ARE FORMED
     Many bolts and machine screws are rolled out by machines between flat or circular thread-rolling dies at the rate of thousands per hour. Other threads are cut in large quantities on metal rods by special types of lathes called automatic screw machines. Where only a few parts are to be threaded or size is a factor, the threads may be cut on an engine lathe with a cutting tool ground to the shape of the desired type of thread.
     Smaller threads may be cut by hand with a *die.* The die is a specially made cutter similar to a nut. Its cutting threads are hardened. Grooves cut in the die allow the metal chips to fall out. The die is held in a holder called a diestock and is turned by hand to cut the thread.

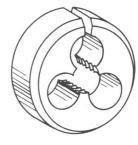

THREAD DIE

HOW INSIDE THREADS ARE CUT
     The tool used to cut an inside thread is called a *tap.* The tap is a hardened cutter similar to a bolt. Grooves cut in its sides allow the metal chips formed in cutting the thread to fall out.
     Before an inside thread is cut, a hole a little larger than the minor diameter is drilled into the metal. A tap drill is used to drill this hole. After the hole has been drilled, the inside thread is cut by forcing and turning the tap into the drilled hole. A tap wrench is used to hold the tap.

TAP

INFORMATION

Thread Terms. The diameter of the cylinder on which the thread is cut is called the crest or major diameter; that at the bottom of the thread is called the root or minor diameter; that midway between the root and crest is called the pitch diameter. The pitch of a thread is the same as the pitch of a helix. It is the distance from the crest of one thread to the crest of the next adjacent thread. The pitch is also sometimes specified by giving the number of threads per inch. The meanings of all of these terms are illustrated in the diagram on the facing page.

PROBLEM

1. Draw a sharp V-thread to the specifications shown:

2. Major diameter = 2-1/2 inches.

3. Length of thread = 3 inches.

4. Label and dimension drawing as shown.

INSTRUCTIONS

1. Draw border lines and title block.

2. Draw profile of a sharp V thread as shown on the facing page.

3. Label as shown—all letters to be 1/8 inch high.

4. Copy the screw thread terminology in your graph notebook.

5. Use 1/8 inch-size lettering.

Screw Thread Terms

The definitions of terms relating to screw-threads are illustrated above.

Screw-thread   A ridge of uniform section in the form of a helix on the external or internal surface of a cylinder.

External thread   A thread on the outside of a member.

Internal thread   A thread on the inside of a member. Example: A thread in a nut.

Major Diameter   The largest diameter of the thread of a screw or nut.

Minor Diameter   The smallest diameter of the thread of a screw or nut.

Pitch   The distance from a point on a screw thread to a corresponding point on the next thread measured parallel to the axis.

Lead   The distance a screw-thread advances axially in one turn. On a single-thread screw, the lead and the pitch are the same; on a double-thread screw the lead is twice the pitch; on a triple-thread screw, the lead is three times the pitch.

Angle of Thread   The angle included between the sides of the thread measured in an axial plane, that is a plane through the axis.

Crest   The surface of a thread joining two sides at the major diameter of a screw and the minor diameter of a nut.

Root   The surface of a thread joining two sides at the minor diameter of a screw and the major diameter of a nut.

Depth   The distance from the root of a thread to a line between two adjacent crests, measured perpendicular to the axis.

Axis   The center line running lengthwise through a screw.

INFORMATION

THREADS. The principal uses of threads are: (1) for fastening, (2) for adjusting, and (3) for transmitting power. Four different forms of threads are shown on the facing page.

The Unified Standard form of screw thread has largely replaced the former American (National) Standard form. It is called Unified because it is the result of an agreement among the United States, the United Kingdom and Canada to unify their respective screw threads to obtain interchangeability.

For the transmission of power and motion, the modified square thread, with slightly sloping sides, which is now rarely used, transmits power parallel to its axis. A still further modification of the square thread is the stronger Acme thread, which is easier to cut and more readily disengages when used for split nuts (as on lead screws for lathes).

PROBLEM

Draw thread profiles of American National, Unified, square, and Acme external threads.

INSTRUCTIONS

1. Draw border lines and title block.

2. Divide page into 4 equal parts.

3. Draw thread profiles as shown.
    1st box, pitch = 1 inch
    2nd box, pitch = 1 1/8 inch
    3rd box, pitch = 1 inch
    4th box, pitch = 1 1/2 inch

Screw Thread Profiles	

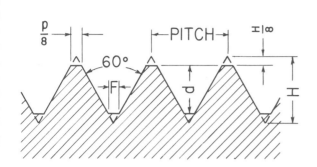

AMERICAN NATIONAL THREAD

H = DEPTH OF SHARP V – TH'D = 0.86603p

$p = \dfrac{1}{\text{NO. TH'DS PER IN.}}$

d = DEPTH = p x 0.64952

$F = \text{FLAT} = \dfrac{p}{8}$

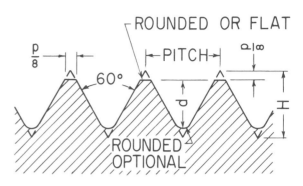

UNIFIED EXTERNAL THREAD

H = DEPTH OF SHARP V – TH'D = 0.86603p

$p = \text{PITCH} = \dfrac{1}{\text{NO. TH'DS PER IN.}}$

$d = \dfrac{0.8660}{N}$

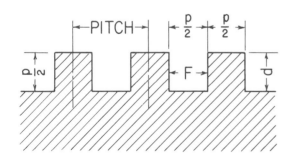

SQUARE THREAD (UNMODIFIED)

$p = \text{PITCH} = \dfrac{1}{\text{NO. TH'DS PER IN.}}$

d = DEPTH = p x 0.500

F = SPACE WIDTH = p x 0.500

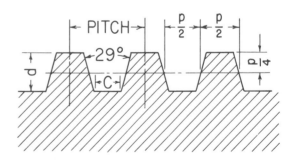

ACME THREAD

$p = \text{PITCH} = \dfrac{1}{\text{NO. TH'DS PER IN.}}$

d = DEPTH = p x 0.500

F = FLAT = 0.3707p – 0.259 (ALLOWANCE)

C = FLAT = 0.3707p – 0.259 (ALLOWANCE)

INFORMATION

When the actual diameter of the thread upon the drawing is 3/4 inch or over, it will look better if the large scale convention is used.

PROBLEM

In your graph notebook, draw thread representations shown on pages 287, 288 and 289.

INSTRUCTIONS

With the aid of a triangle show the stages in drawing threads, that is, leave light construction lines after the thread outline has been darkened.

Drawing the Large-Scale Thread Representation

PITCH = 1 ÷ NO. OF THDS. PER IN.

DIA.

$\frac{p}{2}$　　　　　　　p

1. On the upper line, mark off spaces equal to the pitch. On the lower line mark off one space which is one-half the pitch. Then continue by marking off the full pitch.

60°

60°

2. Using a 60-degree triangle, draw sloping lines from points on upper and lower lines as shown.

60°

60°

3. Reversing the position of the triangle, draw lines sloping in the opposite direction from each point.

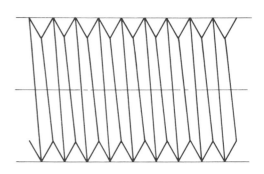

4. Connect the roots and the crests of the thread with slanting lines. Note that the crest and root lines are not parallel. Darken the thread outline.

Drawing an Acme Thread

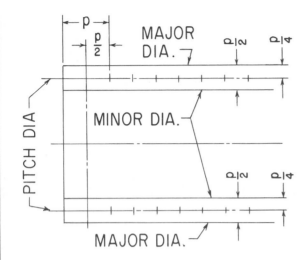

$$\text{Pitch} = \frac{1}{\text{No. thds. per in.}}$$

1. Lay out the major, minor and pitch diameters. The pitch is measured off on the pitch lines as shown.

2. Draw through the marked-off pitch points at 15 degrees to the vertical as shown. Note that a right inclined line at the bottom lies directly below a right inclined line at the top and the same is true for the left inclined lines.

$14\frac{1}{2}°$ (USUALLY DRAWN 15°)

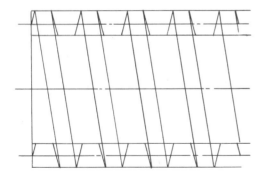

3. Add the crest and root profile lines.

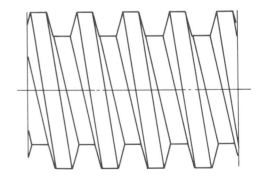

4. Add the root side lines. Darken the thread outline.

Drawing a Square Thread

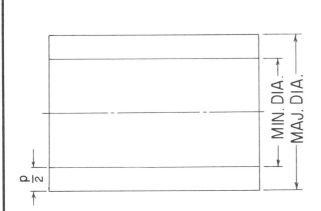

1. Draw the center line, and lay out length and major and minor diameters of thread.

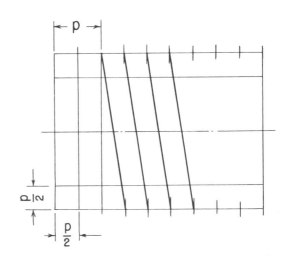

2. Lay off the pitch p and one-half pitch spaces. Draw parallel sides of thread.

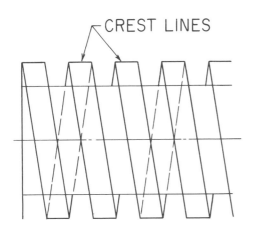

3. Draw the crest lines as shown. Dashed lines show how edge of triangle is held to complete sides of thread at top and bottom. Do not draw dashed lines.

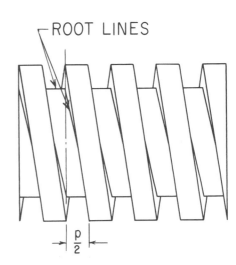

4. Draw the root lines as shown.

INFORMATION

Detailed rendering of threads is time-consuming. Its use is justified only in those few cases where appearance and permanency are important factors, and when it is necessary to avoid the possibility that confusion might result from the use of one of the symbolic methods. The preparation of a detailed representation is a task that belongs primarily to a draftsman.

PROBLEM

Make detailed screw thread representation to specifications shown in the following group on page 291.

INSTRUCTIONS

Draw border lines and title block.

1. On 1st sheet, draw single sharp V-thread to specified dimensions.

2. On 2nd sheet, draw single Acme thread to specified dimensions.

3. On 3rd sheet, draw double square thread to specified dimensions.

4. Use 4H lead for construction lines. Darken thread outline with an H lead.

Practice in Drawing Single Threads

Use 4H lead for construction lines. Darken object lines with H lead.

Note that where a single thread is called for it is not necessary to use the word "single" to specify it. Unless the word "double," "triple," "quadruple," etc., appears, the thread is assumed to be single.

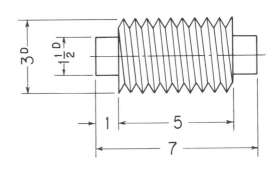

PITCH = $\frac{1}{2}$

V- THREAD

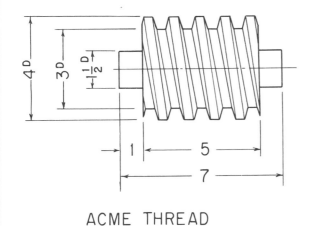

PITCH = 1

ACME THREAD

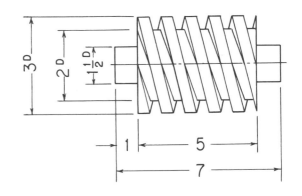

PITCH = $\frac{1}{2}$

SQUARE THREAD

Review Questions

Unit 22 review questions to be answered on a separate sheet of paper.

DIRECTIONS:

For each of the numbered statements below, write the number and after it the figure, symbol, word or words which will complete the sentence. Do NOT write in the book.

1. All screw threads are based upon the curve known as the _____.
   a) fastener
   b) key
   c) helix
   d) stem
   e) root

2. A ridge of uniform section in the form of a helix on the external or internal surface of a cylinder is known as a _____.
   a) helix
   b) diameter
   c) root
   d) crest
   e) thread

3. The surface of a thread joining two sides at the major diameter of a screw and the minor diameter of a nut is a _____.
   a) depth
   b) axis
   c) root
   d) crest
   e) screw

4. The centerline running lengthwise through a screw is an/a _____.
   a) angle
   b) axis
   c) crest
   d) root
   e) depth

5. Outside threads are cut by a/an _____.
   a) screw
   b) tap
   c) drill
   d) die
   e) chip

6. Inside threads are cut by a/an _____.
   a) die
   b) lathe
   c) drill
   d) tap
   e) chip

7. "LH" placed after the designation of the thread is called _____ hand.
   a) bottom
   b) right
   c) middle
   d) side
   e) left

8. Stock may be held in a vise and threaded with a/an _____.
   a) hammer
   b) grind
   c) drill
   d) die
   e) tap

9. The distance from a point on a screw thread to a corresponding point on the next thread measured parallel to the axis is called the _____.
   a) crest
   b) root
   c) depth
   d) pitch
   e) axis

10. The largest diameter of the thread of a screw or nut is the _____ diameter.
    a) major
    b) minor
    c) pitch
    d) lead
    e) screw

INFORMATION

Present-day draftsmen seldom, if ever, draw actual thread shapes unless they are making special display drawings. The demand for speed and economy in making drawings require a quick easily drawn and understandable substitute for a thread.

The two methods used omit the V or other thread shape and show only the root and crest lines. The *conventional* thread drawing uses alternate short heavy and long light lines to show threads. The *simplified* thread drawing uses one row of hidden lines for outside threads and two rows for inside threads.

PROBLEM

Draw simplified external thread symbols in the following group.

INSTRUCTIONS

1. Draw border lines and title block.

2. Divide sheet into 4 equal parts.

3. In the first box draw a simplified external thread symbol following the steps shown on the facing page. Combine all steps into one figure.

Drawing the Simplified Thread Representation

This method of drawing external threads is frequently used to save time, particularly in showing threads of small diameters.

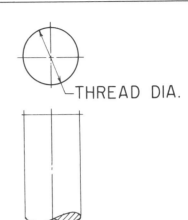

1. Draw thread major diameter in top and front views.

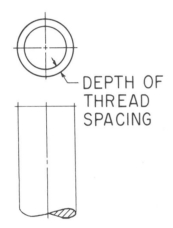

2. In top view show depth of thread.

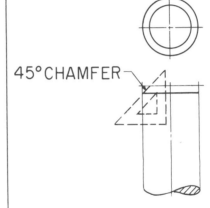

3. The 45° chamfer extends to the root line of the thread.

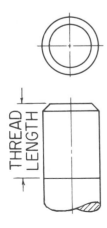

4. Draw the thread length.

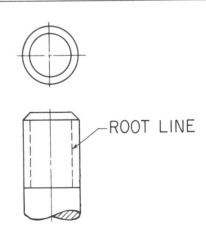

5. Show root lines on thread length.

INFORMATION

The conventional method of thread representation is widely used. It consists of light lines drawn across the diameter to represent the crests and heavy lines drawn part way across the diameter and between the light lines to represent the roots.

PROBLEM

To draw a conventional representation of an external thread.

INSTRUCTIONS

1. In the second box of the sheet previously prepared, draw a conventional representation of an external screw thread. Scale: 2 X size shown on the facing page.

2. Use a 4H pencil for construction lines.

3. Darken object lines with an H pencil.

4. Follow each step shown but combine all steps into one figure.

Drawing the Conventional External Thread Representation

This method of drawing external threads is widely used for sizes up to 1-inch diameter.

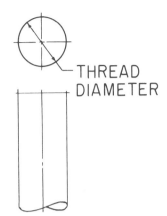

1. Draw thread diameter in top and front views.

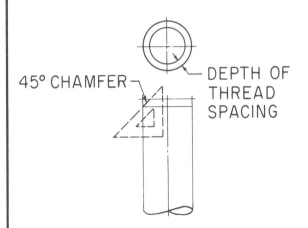

2. Show depth of thread in top view and draw 45-degree chamfer in front view.

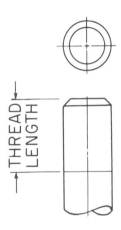

3. The thread length is drawn.

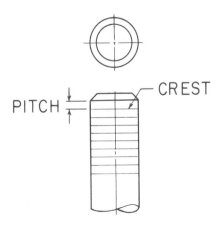

4. Crest lines are spaced by eye or scale.

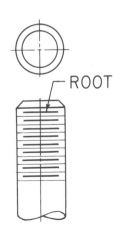

5. Root lines are spaced by eye, and are usually drawn heavier.

INFORMATION

The simplified method of drawing internal threads is similar to that for external threads. The major diameter is the root diameter and hence is shown by a dashed line. The minor diameter is the crest diameter and is shown by a solid line when the view shows the end of the threaded hole. Otherwise it, too, is shown as a dashed line since it is hidden.

PROBLEM

To draw a simplified representation of an internal thread.

INSTRUCTIONS

1. In the third box of the sheet previously prepared, draw a simplified representation of an internal thread. Scale: 2 X size shown on facing page.

2. Use a 4H pencil for construction lines.

3. Darken object lines with an H pencil.

4. Follow each step shown but combine all steps into one figure.

Drawing the Simplified Internal Thread Representation

This method of drawing internal threads is frequently used to save time, particularly in showing threads of small diameters.

1. Draw top and front views.

THREAD DIAMETER

2. In top view show hidden major or root diameter of thread.

DEPTH OF THREAD

3. In top view show depth of thread by drawing visible minor or crest diameter.

4. In front view draw hidden root line.

5. In front view draw hidden crest line.

INFORMATION

The conventional method of drawing internal screw threads is similar to that for external threads. However, in the view showing the end of the threaded hole, the conventional representation is the same as the simplified representation.

PROBLEM

To draw a conventional representation of an internal thread.

INSTRUCTIONS

1. In the fourth box of the sheet previously prepared, draw a conventional representation of an internal thread. Scale: 2 X size shown on the facing page.

2. Use a 4H pencil for construction lines.

3. Darken object lines with an H pencil.

4. Follow each step shown but combine all steps into one figure.

Drawing the Conventional Internal Thread Representation

This method of drawing internal threads is widely used for sizes up to 1-inch diameter.

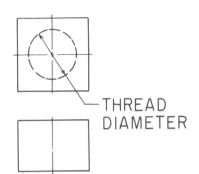

1. Draw top and front views. Show major or root thread diameter in top view.

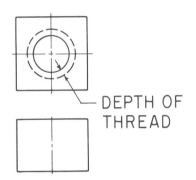

2. In top view show depth of thread by drawing minor or crest diameter.

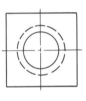

3. In front view draw major diameter.

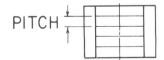

4. The lines representing the crests are spaced by eye or scale to look well and need not conform to the actual thread pitch.

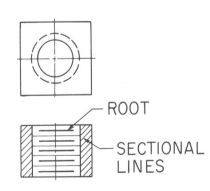

5. In the front view root lines are equally spaced by eye between crest lines and usually drawn heavier. Draw sectional lines.

INFORMATION

This is a review and summary of thread representation methods. The chart on the facing page shows the three methods of representation which you have studied.

Graphic representation shows the threads as they would appear to the eye.

Conventional representation makes use of a pattern of alternating light and dark lines to indicate the thread.

Simplified representation makes use of hidden lines parallel to the axis of the thread to indicate the thread.

The conventional and simplified representations are considered to be standard methods for threads under 1 inch in diameter.

PROBLEM

Draw thread representation summary chart.

INSTRUCTIONS

1. Draw border lines and title block.

2. Draw the entire thread summary chart.

3. All letters are to be 1/8 inch high.

	EXTERNAL THREADS	INTERNAL THREADS
GRAPHIC		
CONVENTIONAL (REGULAR)		HOLE TAPPED THROUGH / TAP DRILL SHOWN
SIMPLIFIED		HOLE TAPPED THROUGH / TAP DRILL SHOWN

Thread Representation Summary Chart

INFORMATION

Threads are designated on mechanical drawings by a standard system of numbers and letter symbols. Thus, a thread designation might read: 1/2-13 UNC-2A. This would indicate that the thread had a 1/2 inch basic diameter and 13 threads per inch. It is in the Unified Coarse Thread Series and is an external thread with a class 2A tolerance. If it were an internal thread, a 2B tolerance symbol would have been used.

Ordinarily, threads are cut so that a clockwise rotation of the screw advances it into the mating piece. Occasionally, however, it is desirable to have counter-clockwise rotation advance the screw. Such threads are called (left-handed) and are designated by the letters LH following the ordinary designation, thus: 1/2-13 UNC-2A-LH.

PROBLEM

Copy the thread designations for the internal and external threads together with the meaning of each part of the designation in your graph notebook.

INSTRUCTIONS

1. Use 1/8-inch high letters.

2. Use a soft H pencil.

Screw Thread Designations

INTERNAL THREAD

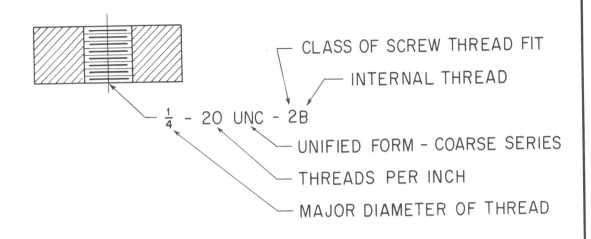

CLASS OF SCREW THREAD FIT

INTERNAL THREAD

$\frac{1}{4}$ - 20 UNC - 2B

UNIFIED FORM - COARSE SERIES

THREADS PER INCH

MAJOR DIAMETER OF THREAD

EXTERNAL THREAD

CLASS OF FIT

EXTERNAL THREAD

$\frac{1}{4}$ - 20 UNF - 2A

MAJOR DIAMETER OF THREAD

THREADS PER INCH

UNIFIED FORM - FINE SERIES

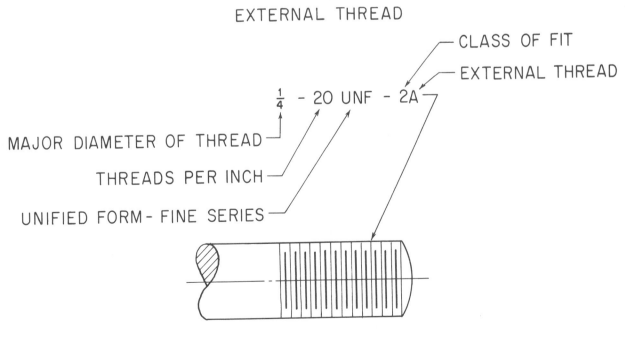

INFORMATION

Screw threads are arranged in various series of small to large diameters. Each series specifies a different number of threads for a given basic diameter. Thus, a 1/2-inch diameter coarse thread (UNC) will have 13 threads per inch, a 1/2-inch diameter fine thread will have 20 threads per inch, and a 1/2-inch diameter extra-fine thread will have 28 threads per inch.

There are also thread series in which all of the diameters have the same number of threads: the 4UN series threads all have 4 threads per inch, the 6UN series threads all have 6 threads per inch and so on.

On the facing page the various series are listed and some of their uses are given.

The diameters and threads per inch for each of these series are given in the table on page 309.

Screw Thread Series—1

1. *UNC*—Coarse thread for general use, quick and easy assembly.

2. *UNF*—Fine thread for general use, high-strength bolting, and for adjusting screws. Used a great deal in aircraft and automobile work.

3. *UNEF*—Extra-fine thread for use with thin-walled tubes where a great many threads per inch are required. Used mainly for aeronautical purposes.

4. *8 UN*—Eight-thread for use on a uniform-pitch series for large diameters. Eight-thread series means eight threads per inch, and is used for diameters larger than one inch.

5. *12 UN*—Twelve-thread for large diameters requiring threads of a medium-fine pitch. The 12 UN series is used for diameters larger than 1-1/2 inches.

6. *16 UN*—Sixteen-thread is a uniform pitch series for large diameters requiring fine-pitch threads such as adjusting collars, or bearing retaining nuts. The 16 UN series is used for diameters larger than 1-11/16 inches.

INFORMATION

Standard machine screws are available in certain stated sizes ranging from No. 0, which has a basic diameter of .0600 inch, to 3/4-inch, which has a basic diameter of .7500 inch. Standard bolts range in size from 1/4 inch basic diameter to 1-1/2, 3 or 4 inches basic diameter depending upon the type. For available sizes of screws, bolts and nuts reference should be made to a standard handbook.

There are a definite number of threads per inch assigned to each diameter. Thus, a No. 0 diameter screw has 80 threads per inch, a 1/4 inch diameter screw or bolt may have 20, 28 or 32 threads per inch, and a 1-1/2 inch diameter bolt may have 6, 12 or 18 threads per inch.

In addition to the standard combinations of diameter and threads per inch, certain special combinations are also available.

The table on the facing page shows the standard combinations of diameters and threads per inch for various Unified Thread Series. The Unified Threads are standard for the United States, Canada and the United Kingdom.

Screw Thread Series—2

Sizes†	Basic Major Diam.	Series with Graded Pitches			Series with Uniform (Constant) Pitches							
		Coarse UNC	Fine UNF	Extra-fine UNEF	4UN	6UN	8UN	12UN	16UN	20UN	28UN	32UN
0	0.0600	..	80	..	..	..	..	..	..	..	..	..
(1)	0.0730	64	72	..	..	..	..	..	..	..	..	..
2	0.0860	56	64	..	..	..	..	..	..	..	..	..
(3)	0.0990	48	56	..	..	..	..	..	..	..	..	..
4	0.1120	40	48	..	..	..	..	..	..	..	..	..
5	0.1250	40	44	..	..	..	..	..	..	..	..	UNC
6	0.1380	32	40	..	..	..	..	..	..	..	..	UNC
8	0.1640	32	36	..	..	..	..	..	..	..	..	UNF
10	0.1900	24	32	..	..	..	..	..	..	..	UNF	UNEF
(12)	0.2160	24	28	32	..	..	..	..	..	UNC	UNF	UNEF
¼	0.2500	20	28	32	..	..	..	..	..	20	28	UNEF
5⁄16	0.3125	18	24	32	..	..	..	..	UNC	20	28	UNEF
3⁄8	0.3750	16	24	32	..	..	..	..	16	UNF	UNEF	32
7⁄16	0.4375	14	20	28	..	..	..	..	16	UNF	UNEF	32
½	0.5000	13	20	28	..	..	..	UNC	16	20	28	32
9⁄16	0.5625	12	18	24	..	..	..	12	16	20	28	32
5⁄8	0.6250	11	18	24	..	..	..	12	16	20	28	32
(11⁄16)	0.6875	..	..	24	..	..	..	12	16	20	28	32
¾	0.7500	10	16	20	..	..	..	12	UNF	UNEF	28	32
(13⁄16)	0.8125	..	..	20	..	..	..	12	16	UNEF	28	32
7⁄8	0.8750	9	14	20	..	..	..	12	16	UNEF	28	32
(15⁄16)	0.9375	..	..	20	..	..	..	12	16	UNEF	28	32
1	1.0000	8	12	20	..	..	UNC	UNF	16	UNEF	28	32
(1 1⁄16)	1.0625	..	..	18	..	..	8	12	16	20	28	..
1 1⁄8	1.1250	7	12	18	..	..	8	UNF	16	20	28	..
(1 3⁄16)	1.1875	..	..	18	..	..	8	12	16	20	28	..
1 ¼	1.2500	7	12	18	..	..	8	UNF	16	20	28	..
(1 5⁄16)	1.3125	..	..	18	..	..	8	12	16	20	28	..
1 3⁄8	1.3750	6	12	18	..	UNC	8	UNF	16	20	28	..
(1 7⁄16)	1.4375	..	..	18	..	6	8	12	16	20	28	..
1 ½	1.5000	6	12	18	..	UNC	8	UNF	16	20	28	..
(1 9⁄16)	1.5625	..	..	18	..	6	8	12	16	20	..	..
1 5⁄8	1.6250	..	..	18	..	6	8	12	16	20	..	..
(1 11⁄16)	1.6875	..	..	18	..	6	8	12	16	20	..	..
1 ¾	1.7500	5	..	..	..	6	8	12	16	20	..	..
(1 13⁄16)	1.8125	..	..	..	..	6	8	12	16	20	..	..
1 7⁄8	1.8750	..	..	..	..	6	8	12	16	20	..	..
(1 15⁄16)	1.9375	..	..	..	..	6	8	12	16	20	..	..
2	2.0000	4½	..	..	..	6	8	12	16	20	..	..
(2 1⁄8)	2.1250	..	..	..	..	6	8	12	16	20	..	..
2 ¼	2.2500	4½	..	..	..	6	8	12	16	20	..	..
(2 3⁄8)	2.3750	..	..	..	..	6	8	12	16	20	..	..
2 ½	2.5000	4	..	..	UNC	6	8	12	16	20	..	..
(2 5⁄8)	2.6250	..	..	..	4	6	8	12	16	20	..	..
2 ¾	2.7500	4	..	..	UNC	6	8	12	16	20	..	..
(2 7⁄8)	2.8750	..	..	..	4	6	8	12	16	20	..	..
3	3.0000	4	..	..	UNC	6	8	12	16	20	..	..
(3 1⁄8)	3.1250	..	..	..	4	6	8	12	16	..	..	..
3 ¼	3.2500	4	..	..	UNC	6	8	12	16	..	..	..
(3 3⁄8)	3.3750	..	..	..	4	6	8	12	16	..	..	..
3 ½	3.5000	4	..	..	UNC	6	8	12	16	..	..	..
(3 5⁄8)	3.6250	..	..	..	4	6	8	12	16	..	..	..
3 ¾	3.7500	4	..	..	UNC	6	8	12	16	..	..	..
(3 7⁄8)	3.8750	..	..	..	4	6	8	12	16	..	..	..
4	4.0000	4	..	..	UNC	6	8	12	16	..	..	..

INFORMATION

The Unified Thread tolerance class symbols are 1A and 1B, 2A and 2B, and 3A and 3B. The tolerance class controls, among other factors, the accuracy with which the thread on the fastener or in the hole is to be made. Classes 1A (external thread) and 1B (internal thread) call for the least accurate threads. Class 2A (external thread) and 2B (internal thread) are most commonly used for general applications including production of bolts, nuts, screws and similar fasteners. Classes 3A (external thread) and 3B (internal thread) call for the most accurate threads.

On the facing page are shown three classes of Unified screw threads.

PROBLEM

Draw the diagram for each class in your graph notebook.

INSTRUCTIONS

1. Use 1/8-inch high letters.

2. Use a soft H pencil.

3. Do not copy the text descriptions.

Screw Thread Classes

Machine screws may have different numbers of threads per inch, and they can fit loosely or tightly into the threaded hole in which they are inserted. The tightness or looseness of the fit depends upon what the screw will be required to do.

The new Unified and American Screw Thread Standards specify three classes. Application of these classes are as follows:

Note: The letter "A" applies to an external thread.
The letter "B" applies to an internal thread.

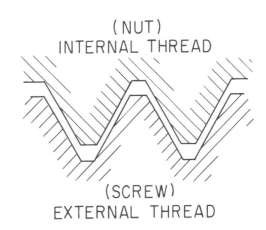

1. Classes 1A and 1B replace Class 1 of the former American Standard. They are used for ordnance and other quick assembly work. They allow for the largest clearance between internal and external threads.

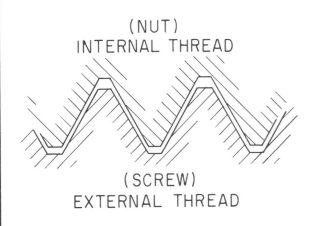

2. Classes 2A and 2B are most commonly made and used. They allow for some clearance between internal and external threads.

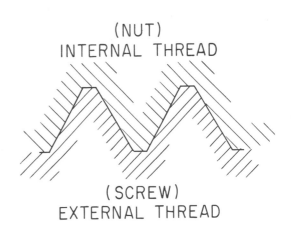

3. Classes 3A and 3B do not allow for any clearance between external and internal threads.

INFORMATION

This is a demonstration lesson in how to use the decimal equivalent chart.

The measurements made in a machine shop are usually taken in inches or fractional parts of an inch. Most of the precision tools in the shop are read in thousandths or ten-thousandths of an inch. The usual graduations on a scale are in 64ths, 32nds, 16ths, and 8ths of an inch.

Before a mechanic can read a scale or the precision-measuring tools efficiently, he must be thoroughly familiar with fractions and decimal fractions. Since he is often called upon to change decimals in reading and checking blue prints and sketches, he should understand this operation thoroughly.

To change a fraction to a decimal, divide the numerator by the denominator. For example, in changing 3/16 to a decimal, 3.0000 ÷ 16 = .1875. The number of digits after the decimal point is the number of *places* to which a decimal is shown, thus, .015 is shown to three decimal places, .0469 is shown to four decimal places, etc. Usually a decimal conversion chart such as that shown on the facing page is referred to. The decimal equivalent is read to two (hundredths), three (thousandths), or four (ten-thousandths) places depending on the accuracy required. The use of a decimal equivalent chart makes arithmetic calculation unnecessary.

Example: Find the decimal equivalent of 1/16 inch to three decimal places.

Answer: .062.

PROBLEMS

1. Find the decimal equivalent of 1/32 of an inch to three places.

2. Find the decimal equivalent of 3/8 of an inch to four places.

3. Find the decimal equivalent of 13/16 of an inch to four places.

Decimal Equivalent Table

Fractions	4 Place	3 Place	2 Place	Fractions	4 Place	3 Place	2 Place
1/64	.0156	.016	.02	33/64	.5156	.516	.52
1/32	.0312	.031	.03	17/32	.5312	.531	.53
3/64	.0469	.047	.05	35/64	.5469	.547	.55
1/16	.0625	.062	.06	9/16	.5625	.562	.56
5/64	.0781	.078	.08	37/64	.5781	.578	.58
3/32	.0938	.094	.09	19/32	.5938	.594	.59
7/64	.1094	.109	.11	39/64	.6094	.609	.61
1/8	.1250	.125	.12	5/8	.6250	.625	.62
9/64	.1406	.141	.14	41/64	.6406	.641	.64
5/32	.1562	.156	.16	21/32	.6562	.656	.66
11/64	.1719	.172	.17	43/64	.6719	.672	.67
3/16	.1875	.188	.19	11/16	.6875	.688	.69
13/64	.2031	.203	.20	45/64	.7031	.703	.70
7/32	.2188	.219	.22	23/32	.7188	.719	.72
15/64	.2344	.234	.23	47/64	.7344	.734	.73
1/4	.2500	.250	.25	3/4	.7500	.750	.75
17/64	.2656	.266	.27	49/64	.7656	.766	.77
9/32	.2812	.281	.28	25/32	.7812	.781	.78
19/64	.2969	.297	.30	51/64	.7969	.797	.80
5/16	.3125	.312	.31	13/16	.8125	.812	.81
21/64	.3281	.328	.33	53/64	.8281	.828	.83
11/32	.3438	.344	.34	27/32	.8438	.844	.84
23/64	.3594	.359	.36	55/64	.8594	.859	.86
3/8	.3750	.375	.38	7/8	.8750	.875	.88
25/64	.3906	.391	.39	57/64	.8906	.891	.89
13/32	.4062	.406	.41	29/32	.9062	.906	.91
27/64	.4219	.422	.42	59/64	.9219	.922	.92
7/16	.4375	.438	.44	15/16	.9375	.938	.94
29/64	.4531	.453	.45	61/64	.9531	.953	.95
15/32	.4688	.469	.47	31/32	.9688	.969	.97
31/64	.4844	.484	.48	63/64	.9844	.984	.98
1/2	.5000	.500	.50	1	1.0000	1.000	1.00

Review Questions

Unit 22 review questions to be answered on a separate sheet of paper.

DIRECTIONS

For each of the numbered statements below, write the number and after it the figure, symbol, word or words which will complete the sentence. Do NOT write in the book.

1. A conventional thread drawing uses the _____ thread drawing method.
   a) middle
   b) alternate
   c) simplified
   d) point
   e) heavy

2. Use a sharp _____H for construction lines.
   a) 2
   b) 4
   c) 3
   d) 1
   e) 5

3. The Unified National Coarse thread series is labelled _____.
   a) NF
   b) UNC
   c) Dia.
   d) F
   e) N

4. The Fine-Thread Series is labelled __ __.
   a) Dia.
   b) NF
   c) FC
   d) 8N
   e) 16N

5. The 8-Pitch Thread Series has _____ threads per inch for all diameters.
   a) 4
   b) 8
   c) 2
   d) 3
   e) 6

Review Questions (continued)

6. A number 0 diameter screw has _____ threads per inch.
   a) 10
   b) 20
   c) 80
   d) 30
   e) 40

7. A 1/4-inch diameter UNC screw has _____ threads per inch.
   a) 10
   b) 20
   c) 15
   d) 30
   e) 5

8. A 1 1/2-inch diameter bolt may have 6, 12 or _____ threads per inch.
   a) 2
   b) 18
   c) 4
   d) 3
   e) 1

9. In the callout, 1/4-20UNC-3A: equals 20 _____ per inch.
   a) screw
   b) root
   c) threads
   d) feet
   e) drill

10. In the callout, 3/4-24UNF-3B: 3/4 is the _____.
    a) diameter
    b) crest
    c) root
    d) die
    e) tap

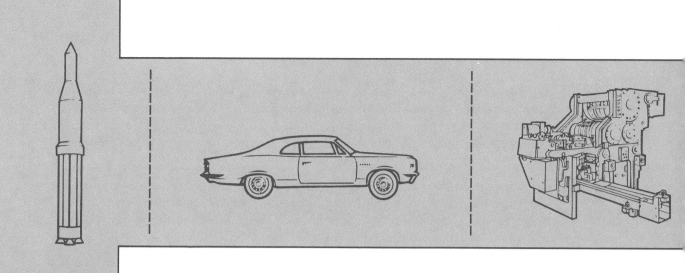

BOLTS, SCREWS AND NUTS

The purpose of this unit is to describe the types and sizes of USA Standards Institute (USASI) standard screws, bolts and nuts in common use and to show how they are drawn.

INFORMATION

Many machine parts must be fastened firmly together, yet in such a manner that they can be taken apart again without great difficulty. This is accomplished with various types of bolts and screws. Bolts differ from screws chiefly in the fact that the bolt is equipped with a nut whereas the screw fastens directly into a tapped hole in one of the parts being held together.

Bolts, screws and nuts have been standardized by the USA Standards Institute. Such standards cover size and shape of bolt or screw head, diameter, number of threads per inch, shape of point, material, etc. The standard sizes of screw fasteners can be obtained most conveniently from a metalworking handbook.

In drawing *square* and *hex* bolts and nuts they are always shown across corners (see drawings on facing page) in all views. This recognized commercial practice (which, however, violates the principles of true projection) prevents confusion of square and hexagonal forms on drawings.

PROBLEM

To draw a square head bolt (called a square bolt) and nut, and a hexagonal head bolt (called a hex bolt) and nut to the following dimensions:

Diameter = 1 inch
Length = 3 inches
Thread length = $1\frac{3}{4}$ inches

INSTRUCTIONS

1. Study the square and hex bolt and nut illustrations on the facing page.

2. Note that the important dimensions for these are given in the table below, while other dimensions, such as radii, are given in the illustrations as multiples or fractions of one or the other of the dimensions shown in the table.

3. Draw border lines and title block.

4. Divide the drawing space into two equal rectangles by a vertical line.

5. In the lefthand space follow the steps for drawing a square bolt and nut as shown on page 320.

6. In the righthand space follow the steps for drawing a hex bolt and nut as shown on page 321.

7. In each case consolidate all steps into one drawing.

8. Under each drawing letter the proper name of the bolt and nut.

Square and Hex Bolts

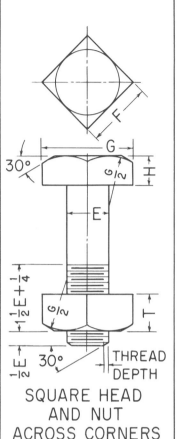

SQUARE HEAD
AND NUT
ACROSS CORNERS

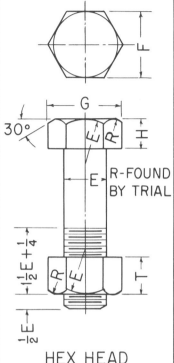

HEX HEAD
AND NUT
ACROSS CORNERS

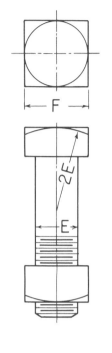

SQ HD & NUT
ACROSS
FLATS

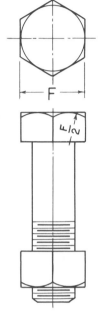

HEX HD & NUT
ACROSS
FLATS

Nominal Dimensions for Drafting Proportions*

E = Diameter of Bolt	1/4	5/16	3/8	7/16	1/2	5/8	3/4	7/8	1	1 1/8	1 1/4	1 3/8	1 1/2
F = Width across Flats (Sq.)	3/8	1/2	9/16	5/8	3/4	15/16	1 1/8	1 5/16	1 1/2	1 11/16	1 7/8	2 1/16	2 1/4
F = Width across Flats (Hex)	7/16	1/2	9/16	5/8	3/4	15/16	1 1/8	1 5/16	1 1/2	1 11/16	1 7/8	2 1/16	2 1/4
G = Width across Corners (Sq.)	1/2	11/16	3/4	7/8	1	1 1/4	1 1/2	1 3/4	2	2 1/4	2 1/2	2 3/4	3
G = Width across Corners (Hex)	1/2	9/16	5/8	11/16	27/32	1 1/16	1 1/4	1 1/2	1 11/16	1 7/8	2 1/8	2 3/8	2 1/2
H = Height of Head	11/64	13/64	1/4	19/64	21/64	27/64	1/2	19/32	21/32	3/4	27/32	29/32	1
T = Thickness of Nut	7/32	17/64	21/64	3/8	7/16	35/64	21/32	49/64	7/8	1	1 3/32	1 13/64	1 5/16

USASI standard square bolts and hex bolts are furnished with Unified Coarse threads, Class 2A (nuts for these bolts have a Class 2B thread). In indicating sizes, therefore, the diameter, length under head, and type of head only need be specified. *Example*: 1/4 x 4 Sq. Hd. Machine Bolt. Another USASI standard bolt, the heavy hex bolt, has a larger head than the regular hex bolt. A note for this type would read, for example, 3/4 x 5 Hvy. Hex Hd. Machine Bolt.

* For exact dimensions see USASI Standard or metalworking handbook.

Drawing Square Bolts and Nuts

The following steps show how a square bolt and nut can be drawn.

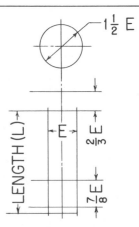

1. Draw outline of bolt and nut proportions along with length.

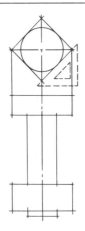

2. In top view circumscribe square around diameter and project down to bolt and nut.

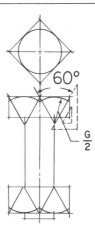

3. With 60-degree triangle locate arcs of bolt head and nut and draw them.

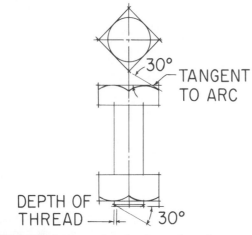

4. With 30-degree triangle draw chamfers tangent to arc.

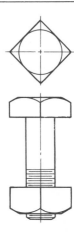

5. Darken object lines and add conventional threads.

Drawing Hex Bolts and Nuts

The following steps show how a hex bolt and nut can be drawn.

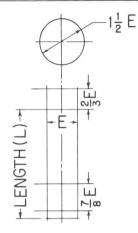

1. Draw outline of bolt and nut proportions.

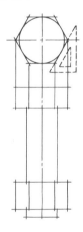

2. In top view circumscribe hex. around diameter and project.

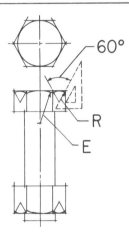

3. With 60-degree triangle locate arcs of bolt head and nut and draw them.

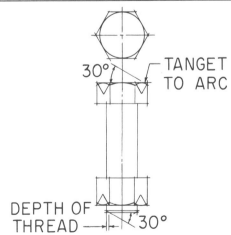

4. With 30-degree triangle draw chamfers tangent to arcs.

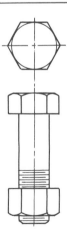

5. Darken object lines and add conventional threads.

INFORMATION

In addition to the *square* and *hex flat nuts* shown on page 319, there are hex nuts which either have a *washer face* on one surface or have all the *corners chamfered* to provide a good bearing surface.

Jam nuts are similar to regular nuts but are thinner. A jam nut is used as a second nut and when run up tight or "jammed" against the first nut, tends to prevent loosening.

Thick nuts are, as the name implies, thicker than regular nuts, and heavy nuts are larger in all external dimensions than regular nuts.

A special class of nuts known as *slotted* and *castle nuts* provide a means for a cotter pin to fit in one of the nut slots as it is slipped through a hole provided in the bolt. This prevents the nut from turning on the bolt.

These types of nuts are shown on the facing page.

PROBLEM

To become familiar with the various types of nuts so that they can be readily identified on sight.

INSTRUCTIONS

Study the various types of nuts shown on the facing page until you can identify each one by its appearance.

Types of Hex Nuts

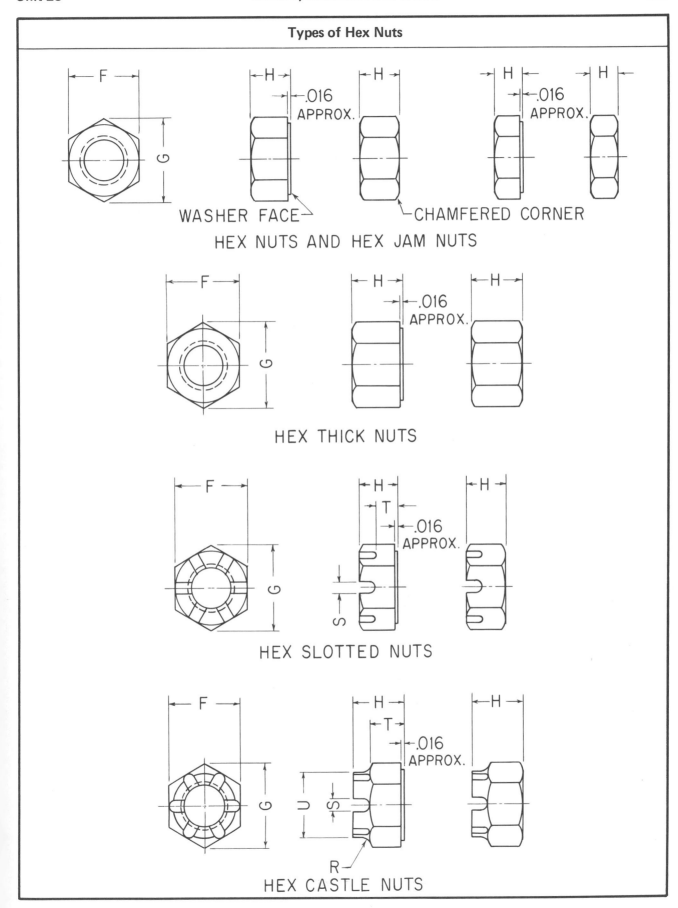

WASHER FACE   CHAMFERED CORNER

HEX NUTS AND HEX JAM NUTS

HEX THICK NUTS

HEX SLOTTED NUTS

HEX CASTLE NUTS

INFORMATION

Cap screws are used in fastening one part to another by passing the screw through a hole in one piece and screwing it into a tapped hole in a second piece. Covers and bearing caps are fastened in place with cap screws. Cap screws resemble bolts, but are not provided with nuts.

There are several styles of heads, the form of which gives a screw its classification. The hexagon cap screw is, in fact, identical with the finished hexagon bolt and can be tightened with a wrench. The socket types (hexagon or fluted) of cap screws require special wrenches or keys. The slotted styles are tightened with a screwdriver and are suitable for use where less strength is required.

The table on the facing page gives a brief summary of cap screw features.

PROBLEM

Draw four cap screws as shown:

> Diameter = 5/8 inch
> Length = $1\frac{1}{4}$ inches
> For screw head dimensions see a handbook.

INSTRUCTIONS

1. Draw border lines and title block.

2. Divide paper into four equal parts.

3. a. In first box, draw a slotted fillister head cap screw.

   b. In second box, draw a hexagon socket flat head cap screw.

   c. In third box, draw a hexagon head cap screw.

   d. In third box, draw a spline socket button head cap screw.

Cap Screws

Cap screws are among the most common of fasteners for metal parts. They are used to fasten two pieces together by passing through the first and screwing into the second. They are manufactured in the Unified Coarse, Unified Fine and 8-thread Series. Cap screws may be used as bolts since the regular nuts will fit them.

Head Types	Features	Materials	Sizes	Description

Hex
Hex and Spline
  Socket Head
Hex and Spline
  Socket Flat Head
Hex and Spline
  Socket Button
  Head
Slotted Head
	General purpose for use in tapped holes	Heat-treated or alloy steel, bronze, brass, corrosion-resistant steel, and aluminum alloy.	No. 0 to 3-inch diameter. Coarse, Fine and 8-thread Series.
			Classes 2A and 3A. Length from 1/4 inch up.
				Headed and threaded.
				End of threaded shank has a chamfer point.

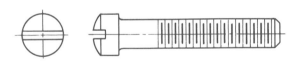

SLOTTED FILISTER HEAD

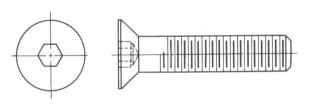

HEX SOCKET FLAT HEAD

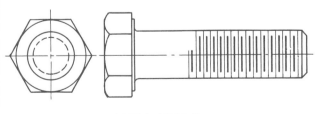

HEX HEAD

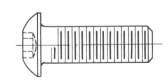

SPLINE SOCKET BUTTON HEAD

INFORMATION

The term "machine screw" is generally understood to mean a screw which enters a tapped hole in a machine part and one having a head that is slotted or recessed to receive a screwdriver. Cap screws are also inserted into tapped holes like machine screws, but are made in larger sizes and are generally used for heavier work.

Standard machine screws come in a wider range of head styles than cap screws and range in size from No. 0 (0.06-inch diameter) to 3/4-inch diameter. Cap screws range from 1/4-inch diameter to 3/4-inch diameter generally; hex head cap screws range up to 3 inches in diameter.

Unless otherwise specified, machine screws are made in the Coarse Thread Series, Class 2A fit.

The table on the facing page gives a brief summary of machine screw features.

PROBLEM

Draw four machine screws as shown on the facing page.

        Diameter = 1/4 inch
        Length = $1\frac{1}{2}$ inches
        For machine screw head proportions see page 329.

INSTRUCTIONS

1. Draw border lines and title block.

2. Divide the sheet into four equal rectangles by a horizontal and a vertical line.

3. In each space draw one of the machine screws shown.

4. Under each one letter the proper title for it.

Machine Screws

MACHINE SCREWS are similar to cap screws but are smaller in diameter. They are usually specified when a fastener less than one-quarter inch in diameter is needed and may be obtained in either steel or brass. They are extensively used in the manufacture of instruments, motors, and the like.

Head Types*	Features	Materials	Sizes	Description

Flat S & CR
Oval S & CR
Round S & CR
Pan S & CR
Filister S & CR
Truss S & CR
Binding S & CR
Hex and Hex
   Washer Plain
   & Slotted
	General purpose for use in tapped holes.	Steel, Brass, Aluminum, Stainless Steel, Silicon, Bronze, Monel, Titanium, & Nylon.	No. 0 to 3/4''.
			Unified Coarse and Fine threads;
			Class 2A.
			Length from 1/8 to 3''.
				Standard purpose, headed & threaded screw. End of threaded shank is usually plain sheared.

FLAT HEAD

OVAL HEAD

ROUND HEAD

FILLISTER HEAD

*S = slotted and CR = cross-recessed.

INFORMATION

On the facing page are shown five different machine screw heads and a brief description of the application of each. Also shown are two types of cross recesses and the common slot which are provided for driving by specially shaped or regular flat bladed screwdrivers. Note the approximate head proportions shown by the simple formulas beside each drawing. Thus, the width A of a round screw head is equal to twice the diameter of the screw. The height of the head is equal to seven-eighths of the diameter of the screw, and the depth of the screw slot is equal to one-half the diameter of the screw. These formulas are given only to guide you in obtaining good head proportions in your drawings.

PROBLEM

To draw the five types of machine screw heads shown on the facing page.

INSTRUCTIONS

1. Make a careful sketch with an H pencil in your graph notebook of each of five machine screw heads shown.

2. Label each.

Machine Screw Head Styles*

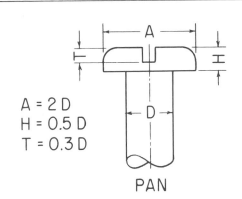

A = 2 D
H = 0.5 D
T = 0.3 D

PAN

1. Used where flat bearing surface but less head height are needed.

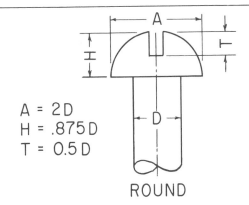

A = 2D
H = .875D
T = 0.5 D

ROUND

2. For general purpose service. Has good slot depth. Used for bolts, machine and cap screws.

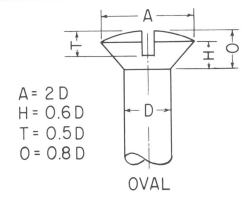

A = 2D
H = 0.6 D
T = 0.5 D
O = 0.8 D

OVAL

3. Similar to standard flat head. Has outer surface rounded for added attractiveness.

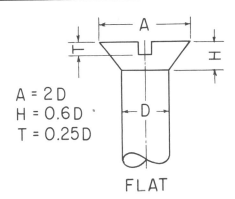

A = 2D
H = 0.6 D
T = 0.25D

FLAT

4. Used where flush surface is desired. Countersunk section aids centering.

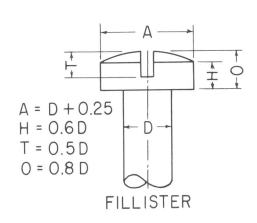

A = D + 0.25
H = 0.6 D
T = 0.5 D
O = 0.8 D

FILLISTER

5. Smaller in diameter than round head, but has same depth of slot. Can be used in c'bored holes.

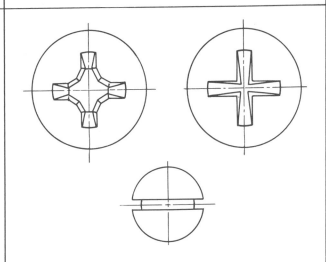

6. Above are shown two types of cross-recesses which require special screwdrivers. The common type of slot is shown below.

*Proportions indicated by formulas are approximate and for representation only.

INFORMATION

A set screw is screwed through one part until its point presses firmly against another part. One example of use is in a tapped hole through the hub of a wheel or gear to hold it on a shaft.

A set screw may have a square head for turning by a wrench or it may be headless with a slot on one end for a screwdriver or a socket (hexagon or spline) to take a driving key. These four types of heads and four types of points are shown on the facing page. Various combinations of heads and points are manufactured. A headless set screw is used where it may be necessary to turn it below the rim of the tapped hole into which it is inserted.

The table on the facing page gives a brief summary of set screw features.

PROBLEM

Draw four 3/4″ x 2″ set screws of the types specified.

For screw head sizes see a handbook.

INSTRUCTIONS

1. Draw border lines and title block.

2. Divide the sheet into four equal rectangles by horizontal and vertical lines.

3. In each space, draw one of the screws in a vertical position.

4. Label each one.

5. Note different types of thread representation use in drawings on facing page. Any of these may be called for depending on the type of drawing. In this exercise use all three.

Set Screws

Setscrews are used to prevent rotary motion between two parts, such as that which tends to occur in the case of a rotating member mounted on a shaft. A set screw is screwed through one part until the point presses firmly against the other part.

Types	Features	Materials	Sizes	Description
Sq. Head Slotted Headless Hex Socket Spline Socket All with various points.	Used for assembling parts to shafts or to hold parts in relative position to each other.	Heat-treated Carbon or Alloy Steel, Stainless Steel, & Brass.	No. 0 to 2". Coarse, & Fine Series. 8-thread Series; Class 2A & 3A.	Fully threaded screw with special pointed end for engagement with mating surface. It is usually employed in a through tapped hole and tightened to high setting torque to provide maximum holding power.

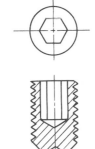

HEXAGON SOCKET, CUP POINT

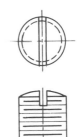

SLOTTED HEADLESS, FLAT POINT

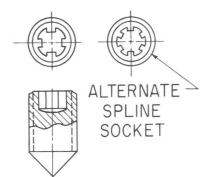

ALTERNATE SPLINE SOCKET

SPLINE SOCKET, CONE POINT

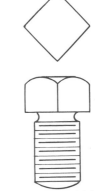

SQUARE HEAD, OVAL POINT

INFORMATION

The drill used for drilling holes to be tapped is called a tap drill. It is usually smaller in diameter than the major diameter of the thread to be tapped. The table on page 334 gives tap drill or bore diameters. For the larger diameters the hole may be bored instead of drilled.

When a table is not available to find the diameter of a tap drill for a given thread, an approximate diameter can be found by subtracting from the outside diameter of the tap an amount equal to 1 divided by the number of threads. The nearest commercial size of drill is then selected. *Example:* Find the tap drill size for a 1/4–20 thread. 1/4 – 1/20 = .25 – .05 = .20. Use a No. 7 drill which is .201 inch in diameter.

When a bolt or screw is used to fasten one part to another, the hole in the untapped part is drilled slightly larger than the outside or body diameter of the screw, hence the drill used is known as a clearance drill. Diameters of clearance drills will also be found in the following table.

When the screw head is to be seated beneath the surface of the part to be held, a counterbore is used to provide a hole large enough in diameter to clear the head of the screw or the lock washer or plain washer underneath the screw head, if used. Sometimes a small surface or spot is provided on a casting or forging so that the underside of the screw head will seat properly. Counterbore and spot facing diameters are also given in the following table.

PROBLEM

Draw proportions for a 3/8-inch tapped hole.

INSTRUCTIONS

1. Draw border lines and title block.

2. For proportions for tapped holes, see chart on facing page.

3. Use the 3/8-inch diameter thread size.

Holes for Tapped Threads

Note: Holes for tapped threads are drilled right through work wherever possible. Where a blind hole is required, its depth depends on strength and holding factors. Usually a clearance depth below the fastener, when fully seated, equal to the diameter of the fastener is desirable.

The length of the fastener should be determined to the nearest commercial length that will allow it to fulfill minimum conditions. A handbook should be consulted.

Use chart on page 334 to obtain tap drill sizes and root diameters of threads.

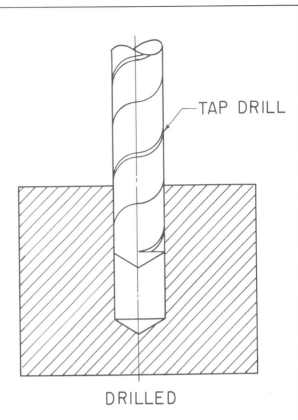

DRILLED

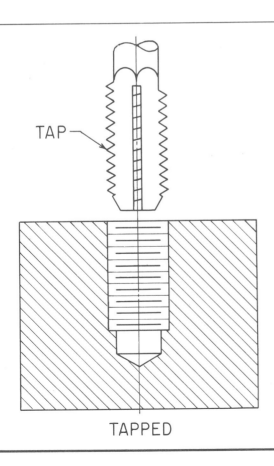

TAPPED

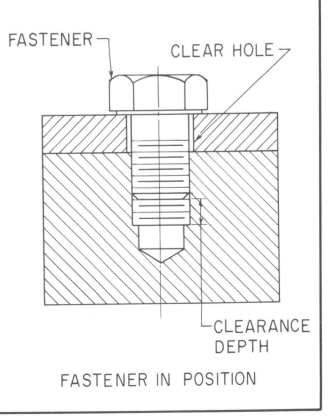

FASTENER IN POSITION

Proportions for Tapped Holes

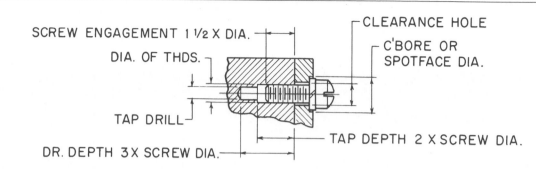

Thd. Diam. and Screw No.	Thds. Per Inch	Tap Drill or Bore Diam.		Depth		Clearance Drill		Counterbore or Spot Face Diam.		
		No.	Dec.	Dr.	Tap	No.	Dec.	No Wash.	Lock Wash.	Plain Wash.
.060 #0	80	3/64	.046	3/16	1/8	50	.070	1/8	. . .	. . .
.073 #1	64	53	.059	7/32	5/32	43	.089	5/32	3/16	. . .
	72	53	.059							
.086 #2	56	50	.070	9/32	3/16	37	.104	3/16	3/16	9/32
	64	50	.070							
.099 #3	48	5/64	.078	5/16	7/32	31	.120	3/16	7/32	9/32
	56	45	.082							
.112 #4	40	43	.089	11/32	1/4	9/64	.140	7/32	1/4	3/8
	48	42	.093							
.138 #6	32	36	.106	7/16	9/32	19	.166	9/32	9/32	1/2
	40	33	.113							
.164 #8	32	29	.136	1/2	11/32	10	.193	5/16	5/16	1/2
	36	29	.136							
.190 #10	24	25	.149	19/32	3/8	7/32	.218	11/32	3/8	17/32
	32	21	.159							
1/4	20	7	.201	3/4	1/2	9/32	.281	7/16	9/16	11/16
	28	3	.213					. . .	3/4	3/4
5/16	18	F	.257	15/16	5/8	11/32	.343	. . .	13/16	13/16
	24	I	.272							
3/8	16	5/16	.312	1 1/8	3/4	13/32	.406	. . .	15/16	15/16
	24	Q	.332							
1/2	13	. . .	.4218	1 1/2	1	9/16	.562	. . .	1 1/4	1 1/4
	20	. . .	.4531							
5/8	11	. . .	.5312	1 7/8	1 1/4	11/16	.687	. . .	1 1/2	1 1/2
	18	. . .	.5781							
3/4	10	. . .	.6562	2 1/4	1 1/2	13/16	.812	. . .	1 5/8	1 5/8
	16	. . .	.6875							
7/8	9	. . .	.7656	2 5/8	1 3/4	15/16	.937	. . .	1 3/4	1 13/16
	14	. . .	.8125							
1	8	. . .	.8750	3	2	1 1/16	1.062	. . .	2	2 1/16
	14	. . .	.9375							
1 1/4	7	. . .	1.1094	3 3/4	2 1/2	1 5/16	1.312	. . .	2 1/2	2 9/16
	12	. . .	1.1718							

Drawing Studs

INFORMATION

A stud is a rod threaded on both ends, and is used when through bolts are not suitable for parts that must be removed frequently, such as cylinder heads, chest covers, etc. The threads on each end may or may not be the same.

PROBLEM

Draw studs to given dimensions.

INSTRUCTIONS

1. Draw border lines and title block.
2. Divide the paper into three equal horizontal parts.
3. Draw the three studs to dimensions specified and dimension each as shown.

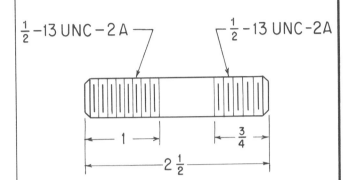

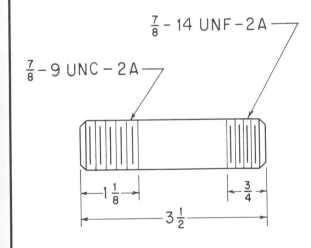

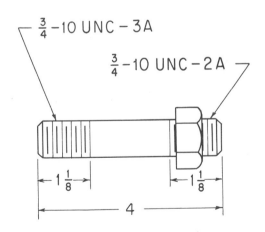

PROBLEM

Draw two bolts to the specifications given.

INSTRUCTIONS

1. Draw border lines and title block.

2. Divide the page into two equal parts vertically.

3. In the first part on the center lines shown, draw top and side views of a
   7/8 – UNC – 2A x 4 inch long semi-finished hexagon head bolt.

4. In the second part on the center line shown, draw top and side views of a
   $1\frac{1}{8}$ – UNC – 2A x 4 inch long square head bolt.

Drawing Hex Head and Square Head Bolts

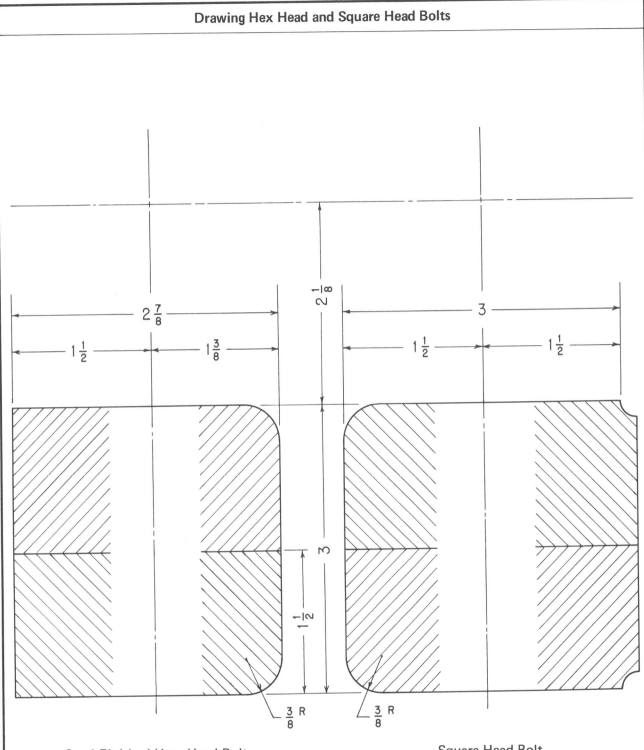

Semi-Finished Hex. Head Bolt   Square Head Bolt

PROBLEM

Draw threaded hole and cap screw to specifications given.

INSTRUCTIONS

1. Draw border lines and title block.

2. Divide the page with a horizontal line into two equal parts.

3. In the first part draw the center lines shown in the top diagram. On these center lines draw front and side views of a 1/2–13 UNC–2B threaded hole using the conventional thread representation. Show the right side view in full section. Dimension the hole according to conventional practices. (Tap drill size is 27/64.)

4. In the second part draw the center line shown in the bottom diagram. On this center line draw a profile view of a 3/4–10 UNC–2A x $2\frac{1}{2}$ round head cap screw using the graphic thread representation. (Thread length - $1\frac{3}{4}$ inches. Head dimensions: height - 17/32 inch, diameter - $1\frac{1}{4}$ inches.)

Drawing a Tapped Hole and a Cap Screw

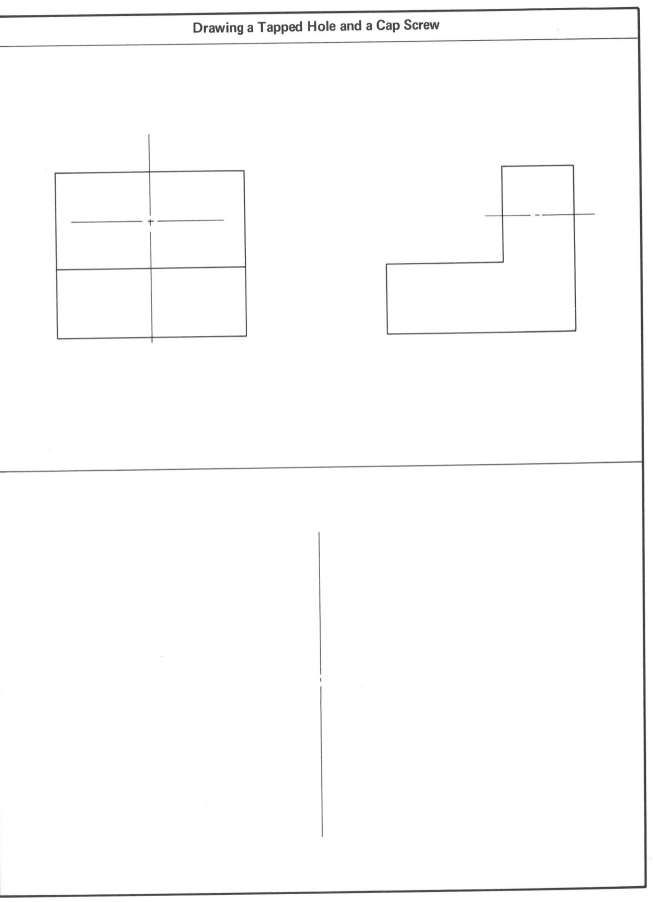

PROBLEM

Draw machine screws and set screws to the specifications given.

INSTRUCTIONS

1. Draw the border lines and title blocks.

2. Divide the paper into four equal parts.

3. In the first part draw a 3/8-inch flat head machine screw, $1\frac{1}{2}$ inches long.

4. In the second part draw a 7/16 inch filister head machine screw, $1\frac{1}{2}$ inches long.

5. In the third part draw a 1/2-inch slotted headless set screw, 7/8 inch long.

6. In the fourth part draw a 9/16-inch square head set screw, $1\frac{1}{8}$ inches long.

Drawing Machine Screws and Set Screws

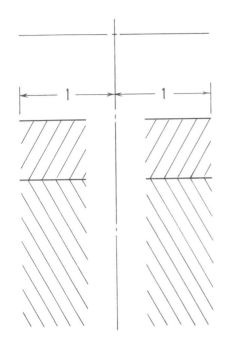

3/8 Flat head machine screw, 1½" long

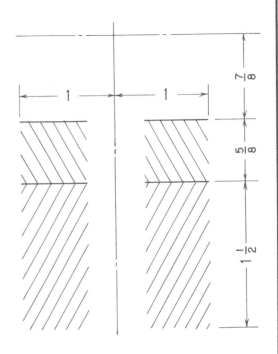

7/16 Fillister head machine screw, 1½" long

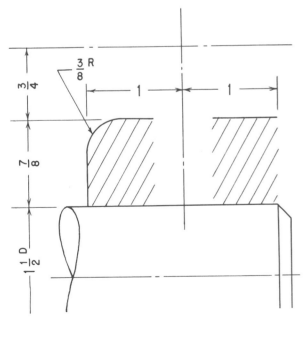

1/2 Headless setscrew, ⅞" long

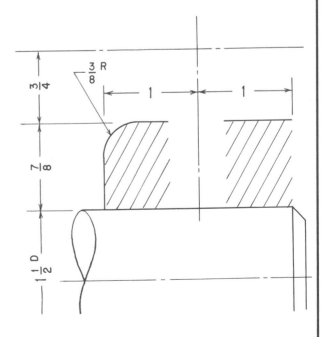

9/16 Square head setscrew, 1⅛" long

Review Questions

Unit 23 review questions to be answered on a separate sheet of paper.

DIRECTIONS

For each of the numbered statements below, write the number and after it the figure, symbol, word or words which will complete the sentence. Do NOT write in the book.

1. A temporary fastener is called a _____.
   a. weld
   b. rivet
   c. screw
   d. hammer
   e. file

2. Wood screws are used only to fasten _____ members.
   a. iron
   b. steel
   c. wood
   d. aluminum
   e. plastic

3. Hex bolts are made in sizes from 1/4 inch to _____ inches.
   a. 1
   b. 2
   c. 3
   d. 4
   e. 5

4. Cap screws are made in sizes from #0 to _____ inches.
   a. 1/2
   b. 3/4
   c. 1
   d. $1\frac{1}{4}$
   e. $1\frac{1}{2}$

5. A stud is a bolt _____ a head.
   a. near
   b. without
   c. with
   d. inside
   e. outside

6. N. F. means National _____.
   a. first
   b. fun
   c. feel
   d. fine
   e. flair

Review Questions (continued)

7. Pitch is the distance between corresponding points on adjacent thread
   forms measured _____ to the axis.
   a. oblique
   b. parallel
   c. equal
   d. opposite
   e. near

8. A hexagon has _____ sides.
   a. 2
   b. 4
   c. 6
   d. 8
   e. 3

9. Machine screws are similar to cap screws but are _____
   in diameter.
   a. larger
   b. similar
   c. smaller
   d. wider
   e. heavier

10. Machine screws come in two series – Coarse and _____
    thread series.
    a. rough
    b. soft
    c. fine
    d. hard
    e. medium

KEYS AND KEYSEATS

The purpose of this unit is to present the various forms of keys and keysets and the ways in which they are drawn.

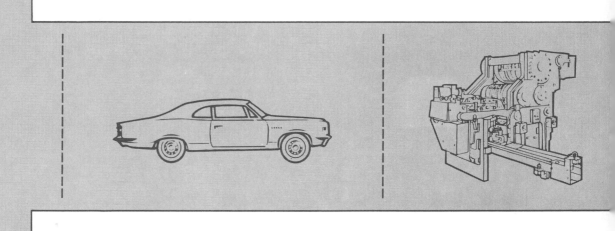

INFORMATION

In machine construction, keys are used to fasten pulleys, cranks, gears, etc., to shafts. Many keys are square or rectangular in cross section. This type of key is inserted into a slot called a keyseat formed partly in the shaft and partly in the hub of the gear, pulley, etc., which is to be fastened to the shaft.

A parallel key has its upper and lower surfaces parallel to each other. A taper key has a taper on its upper surface. Such a taper is commonly 1/8 inch per foot, which means that for every foot in length the depth dimension from top to bottom of the key increases 1/8 inch.

The USA Standards Institute has established standard sizes of keys of various types and of keyseats into which they are to be inserted. In selecting a key for a given shaft, reference is made to tables of sizes given in the USASI Standard or in a metal-working handbook.

Four common types of keys are shown on the facing page.

PROBLEM

Make a drawing of the four common types of keys.

INSTRUCTIONS

1. Draw border lines and title block.

2. Divide paper into four equal sections.

3. In each section draw one of the keys shown.

4. Insert dimension letters in each drawing and letter the name of the key under each one.

5. Make all drawings the same size as shown and take necessary dimensions directly from the illustrations.

Common Types of Keys

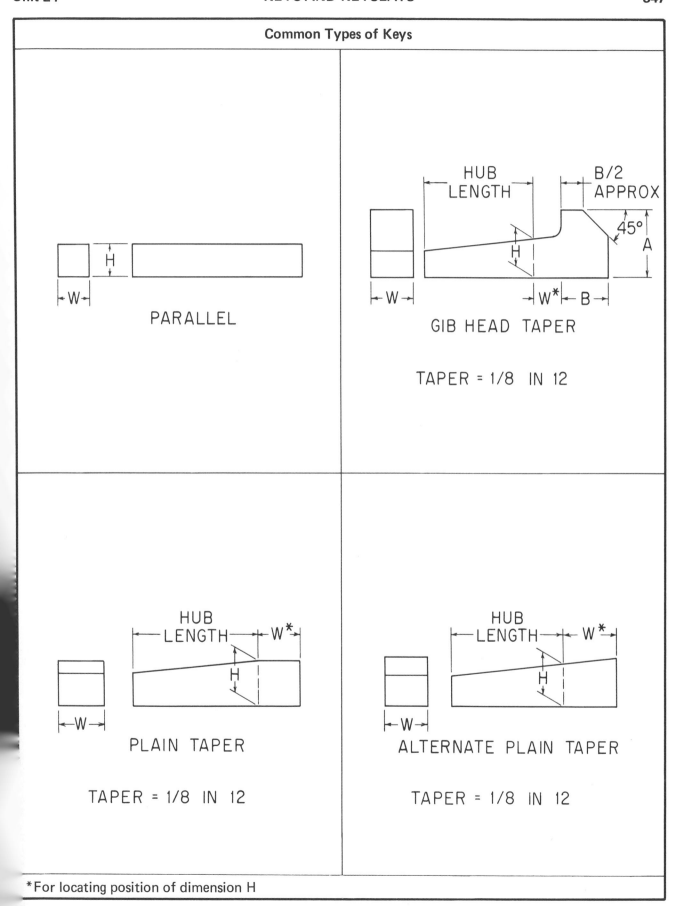

PARALLEL

GIB HEAD TAPER

TAPER = 1/8 IN 12

PLAIN TAPER

TAPER = 1/8 IN 12

ALTERNATE PLAIN TAPER

TAPER = 1/8 IN 12

*For locating position of dimension H

INFORMATION

The simplest key, geometrically, is the square key which fits into a square slot formed by the keyseats in shaft and hub. It is often used to fasten pulleys to motor shafts. It also has many applications in the home workshop. Occasionally, a set screw may be inserted through the hub to keep the square key from coming loose. A similar key is a flat key which is rectangular in cross-section and is used in the same manner as a square key. Square keys are preferred for shafts up through $6\frac{1}{2}$-inches in diameter; rectangular keys for larger shafts.

PROBLEM

Make a drawing of the square key.

INSTRUCTIONS

1. In your graph notebook draw the oblique view of the square key, the end view of the hub and the side view of the shaft with keyseats as shown on the facing page.

2. For dimensioning width and depth of keyseats use dimensions given in table for 1-inch diameter of shaft. Take all other dimensions directly from the illustrations.

The Square Key and Keyseat

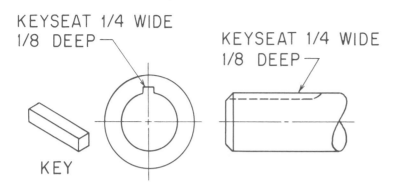

KEYSEAT 1/4 WIDE
1/8 DEEP

KEYSEAT 1/4 WIDE
1/8 DEEP

KEY

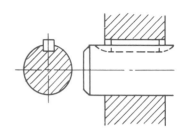

Square Key and Keyseat Dimensions

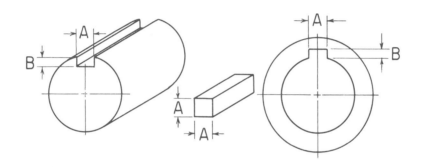

Dia. of Shaft	Width A	Depth B	Dia. of Shaft	Width A	Depth B
$1/2$	$1/8$	$1/16$	$1\,3/8$	$3/8$	$3/16$
$9/16$	$1/8$	$1/16$	$1\,1/2$	$3/8$	$3/16$
$5/8$	$5/32$	$5/64$	$1\,5/8$	$3/8$	$3/16$
$3/4$	$3/16$	$3/32$	$1\,3/4$	$7/16$	$7/32$
$7/8$	$3/16$	$3/32$	$1\,7/8$	$1/2$	$1/4$
1	$1/4$	$1/8$	2	$1/2$	$1/4$
$1\,1/8$	$5/16$	$5/32$	$2\,1/2$	$5/8$	$5/16$
$1\,1/4$	$5/16$	$5/32$	3	$3/4$	$3/8$

INFORMATION

The gib head key, so called because of the shape of the end or head, is tapered on its upper surface. It is inserted into the keyseats of both shaft and hub and driven into place to form a tight and secure fastening. The gib head provides a convenient means of both inserting and removing the key.

Note that because the keyseat is frequently cut with a round milling cutter, it may have one end rounded as shown in the upper lefthand illustration on the facing page.

PROBLEM

Make a drawing of the gib head key.

INSTRUCTIONS

1. In your graph notebook draw the oblique view of the gib head key, the end view of the hub and side view of the shaft showing the keyseats.

2. Draw the end view of the shaft and the cross sectional view of the shaft and hub showing the key in place.

3. Insert the key and keyseat dimensions shown as typical ways of giving these dimensions on the drawing. Note the different notes which may be used.

4. Study the table of gib head key dimensions so that by referring to the diagrams above the table you can identify each dimension given.

The Gib Head Key and Keyseat

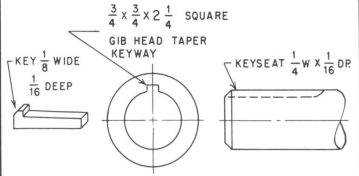

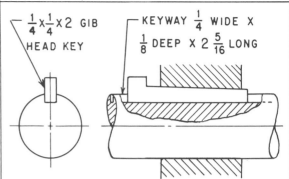

Gib Head Key Dimensions

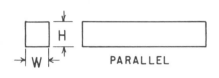

PLAIN AND GIB HEAD

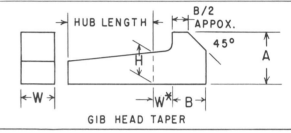

GIB HEAD TAPER

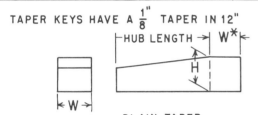

PLAIN TAPER

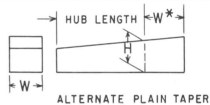

ALTERNATE PLAIN TAPER

Key Size	Square			Rectangular		
Width W	H	A	B	H	A	B
$\frac{1}{8}$	$\frac{1}{8}$	$\frac{1}{4}$	$\frac{1}{4}$	$\frac{3}{32}$	$\frac{3}{16}$	$\frac{1}{8}$
$\frac{3}{16}$	$\frac{3}{16}$	$\frac{5}{16}$	$\frac{5}{16}$	$\frac{1}{8}$	$\frac{1}{4}$	$\frac{1}{2}$
$\frac{1}{4}$	$\frac{1}{4}$	$\frac{7}{16}$	$\frac{3}{8}$	$\frac{3}{16}$	$\frac{5}{16}$	$\frac{5}{16}$
$\frac{5}{16}$	$\frac{5}{16}$	$\frac{1}{2}$	$\frac{7}{16}$	$\frac{1}{4}$	$\frac{7}{16}$	$\frac{3}{8}$
$\frac{3}{8}$	$\frac{3}{8}$	$\frac{5}{8}$	$\frac{1}{2}$	$\frac{1}{4}$	$\frac{7}{16}$	$\frac{3}{8}$
$\frac{1}{2}$	$\frac{1}{2}$	$\frac{7}{8}$	$\frac{5}{8}$	$\frac{3}{8}$	$\frac{5}{8}$	$\frac{1}{2}$
$\frac{5}{8}$	$\frac{5}{8}$	1	$\frac{3}{4}$	$\frac{7}{16}$	$\frac{3}{4}$	$\frac{9}{16}$
$\frac{3}{4}$	$\frac{3}{4}$	$1\frac{1}{4}$	$\frac{7}{8}$	$\frac{1}{2}$	$\frac{7}{8}$	$\frac{5}{8}$
$\frac{7}{8}$	$\frac{7}{8}$	$1\frac{3}{8}$	1	$\frac{5}{8}$	1	$\frac{3}{4}$
1	1	$1\frac{5}{8}$	$1\frac{1}{8}$	$\frac{3}{4}$	$1\frac{1}{4}$	$\frac{7}{8}$
$1\frac{1}{4}$	$1\frac{1}{4}$	2	$1\frac{7}{16}$	$\frac{7}{8}$	$1\frac{3}{8}$	1
$1\frac{1}{2}$	$1\frac{1}{2}$	$2\frac{3}{8}$	$1\frac{3}{4}$	1	$1\frac{5}{8}$	$1\frac{1}{8}$

* For locating position of dimension H

INFORMATION

The Woodruff key is a segment (less than half) of a disk. The circular part of the key seats in a circular recess in the shaft, and the flat edge fits in a slot in the hub as shown on the facing page. This type of key may be modified to have a flat on the bottom, flat ends or both as shown on the facing page.

A circular cutter is used to sink or cut the keyseat in the shaft. In the table on the facing page the diameter C of the cutter and the length D and depth E of cut for a given key and also the over-all height F of the key are given. The number of the key indicates the size of cutter used for its keyseat. The first part of the number gives the width of the cutter in thirty-seconds of an inch and the second part, the diameter of the cutter in eighths of an inch, thus:

$$404 = 4 \times 1/32 = 1/8 \text{ inch wide, and}$$
$$4 \times 1/8 \ = 1/2 \text{ inch diameter}$$

$$1210 = 12 \times 1/32 = 3/8 \text{ inch wide, and}$$
$$10 \times 1/8 \ = 1\text{-}1/4 \text{ inches diameter.}$$

PROBLEM

Make a drawing of the Woodruff key.

INSTRUCTIONS

1. In your graph notebook draw the isometric view of the Woodruff key, the end view of the hub and side view of the shaft showing the keyseat.

2. Draw the end view of the shaft and cross sectional view of the hub and shaft showing the key in place.

3. Letter in the key and keyseat dimensions shown, as typical ways of giving these dimensions on drawings.

4. Study the table of Woodruff keyseat dimensions so that by referring to the diagrams above the table you can identify each dimension given.

Woodruff Key and Keyseat

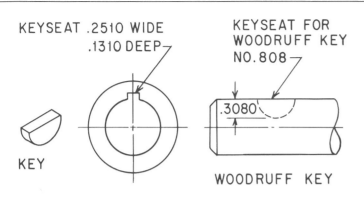

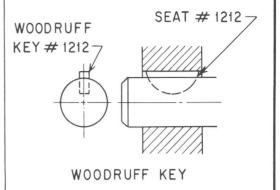

Woodruff Keyseat Dimensions

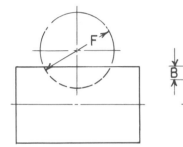 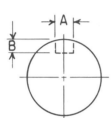 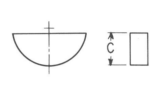 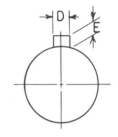

Number of Key	Dia. of Cutter	Keyseat in Shaft			Keyseat in Hub	
		Width of Keyseat	Depth of Keyseat	Height of Key	Width of Key Seat	Depth of Keyseat
	F	A	B	C	D	E
202	$1/4$	$1/16$	.0728	$7/64$	.0635	.0372
303	$3/8$	$3/32$	.1202	$11/64$	.0948	.0529
404	$1/2$	$1/8$	.1355	$13/64$	.1260	.0685
505	$5/8$	$5/32$	.1669	$1/4$	.1573	.0841
606	$3/4$	$3/16$	.2143	$5/16$	.1885	.0997
607	$7/8$	$3/16$	.2763	$3/8$	.1885	.0997
808	1	$1/4$	.3080	$7/16$	.2510	.1310
1009	$1 1/8$	$5/16$	.3228	$31/64$	.3135	.1622
1010	$1 1/4$	$5/16$	.3858	$35/64$	.3135	.1622
1210	$1 1/4$	$3/8$	.3545	$35/64$	.3760	.1935
1212	$1 1/2$	$3/8$	.4485	$41/64$	.3760	.1935

Review Questions

Unit 24 review questions to be answered on a separate sheet of paper.

DIRECTIONS

For each of the numbered statements below, write the number and after it the figure, symbol, word or words which will complete the sentence. Do NOT write in the book.

1. Keys are used to fasten wheels to _____.
   a. windows
   b. doors
   c. shafts
   d. rooms
   e. stairs

2. The gib head key is tapered on its _____ surface.
   a. lower
   b. bottom
   c. side
   d. upper
   e. right side

3. The number of a Woodruff key tells the size of the keyway _____.
   a. screw
   b. portion
   c. cutter
   d. fit
   e. size

4. A key is a block of steel used to secure a rotating member to its _____.
   a. thread
   b. assembly
   c. screw
   d. hub
   e. shaft

5. A keyseat is a slot cut in the hub of a rotating part and in a shaft to permit a _____ to be inserted.
   a. wheel
   b. piston
   c. washer
   d. shaft
   e. key

6. Gib head, square and Woodruff are types of _____.
   a. motors
   b. assemblies
   c. gears
   d. keys
   e. mounts

Review Questions (continued)

7. The Woodruff key is a flat segmental disk with either a flat or _____ bottoms.
   a. square
   b. triangular
   c. hexagonal
   d. round
   e. soft

8. The square key is placed half in the shaft and half in the _____.
   a. piston
   b. handwheel
   c. assembly
   d. pin
   e. hub

9. The square key is generally used to fasten a motor pulley to a motor _____.
   a. seat
   b. end
   c. shaft
   d. piston
   e. hub

10. What is the customary amount of taper in a plain taper key?

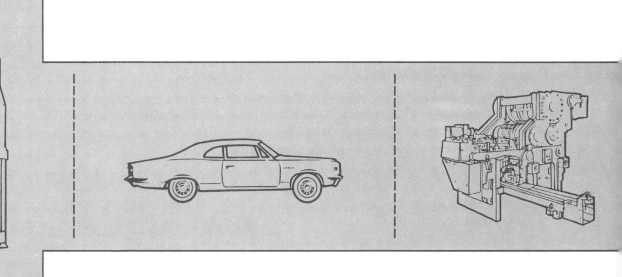

UNIT 25

ASSEMBLY AND DETAIL DRAWINGS

The purpose of this unit is to show how to make
assembly and detail drawings.

INFORMATION

Assembly drawing. A drawing that shows the parts of a machine or machine unit assembled in their relative working positions is an assembly drawing. There are several types of such drawings: design assembly drawings, working assembly drawings, unit assembly drawings, installation diagrams.

Detail drawing. A drawing of a single object showing size, shape and specifications.

PROBLEM

Make assembly and detail drawings of objects in the following group.

INSTRUCTIONS

1. Use a separate sheet for each assembly and detail drawing.

2. Draw border lines and title block on each sheet.

3. It is preferable to use a full-size scale.

4. First make a freehand sketch, showing the number and arrangement of views you plan to use. Include a space for the parts list.

5. After having your sketch approved by your instructor, you may proceed to make your drawing with instruments.

6. For assembly drawings:
   a. Each part is drawn accurately in its place.
   b. Identify each part with 3/8-inch balloons and 3/16-inch high numbers.
   c. A parts list is to be shown.
   d. Show over-all length, width, and height dimensions.
   e. Hidden lines are usually omitted.

7. For detail drawings:
   a. Show necessary views, dimensions, and specifications.
   b. Each part is identified by the balloon number assigned to it in the assembly drawing.

Lathe Clamp

Assignment No. 1

Make assembly and detail drawings of lathe clamp. Use your own judgment for layout of details.

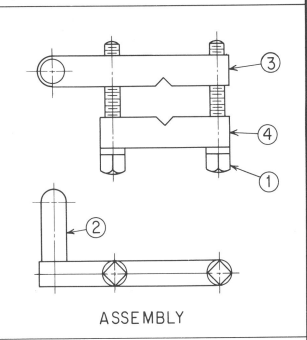

ASSEMBLY

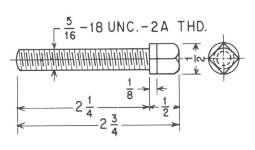

$\frac{5}{16}$ -18 UNC.-2A THD.

① SCREW

NOTE: ALL MATERIAL IS C.R.S.

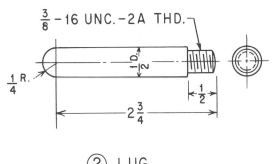

$\frac{3}{8}$ -16 UNC.-2A THD.

② LUG

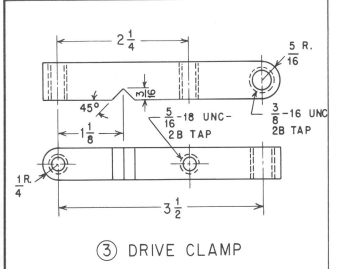

$2\frac{1}{4}$

$\frac{5}{16}$ R.

$45°$

$\frac{3}{16}$

$\frac{5}{16}$ -18 UNC-2B TAP

$\frac{3}{8}$ -16 UNC 2B TAP

$1\frac{1}{8}$

$\frac{1}{4}$ R.

$3\frac{1}{2}$

③ DRIVE CLAMP

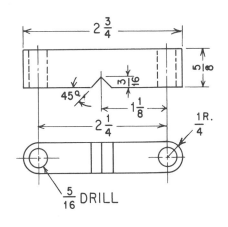

$2\frac{3}{4}$

$\frac{5}{8}$

$45°$

$\frac{3}{16}$

$1\frac{1}{8}$

$2\frac{1}{4}$

1 R. $\frac{1}{4}$

$\frac{5}{16}$ DRILL

④ HOLDING CLAMP

Screwdriver

Assignment No. 2

Make assembly and detail drawings of screwdriver. Include parts list on assembly drawing.

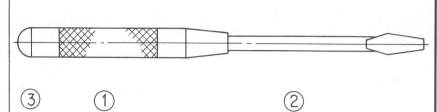

ASSEMBLY

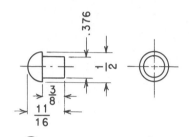

③ CAP – 1 REQ'D – C.R.S.

NOTE: DRIVE FIT IN HANDLE

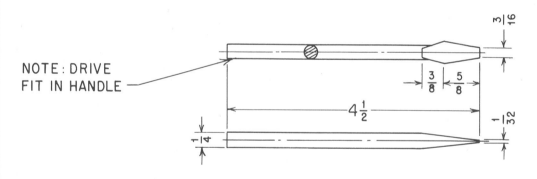

② BLADE – I REQ'D – DRILL ROD

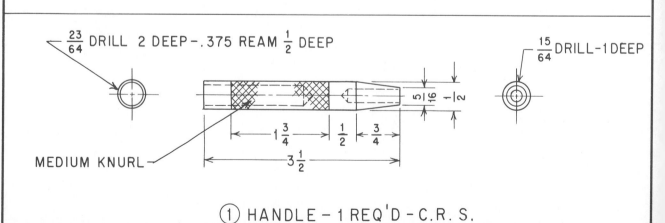

① HANDLE – 1 REQ'D – C.R.S.

Layout Punch

NO.	NAME	MAT.	REQ.
1	CAP	STEEL	1
2	WEIGHT	STEEL	1
3	SHANK	STEEL	1
4	POINT	STEEL	1

Assignment No. 3

Make assembly and detail drawings of layout punch. Include parts list.

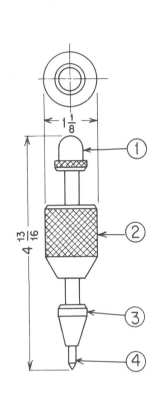

ASSEMBLY

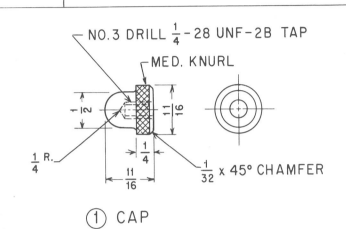

NO.3 DRILL $\frac{1}{4}$ – 28 UNF–2B TAP

MED. KNURL

$\frac{1}{4}$ R.

$\frac{1}{32}$ x 45° CHAMFER

① CAP

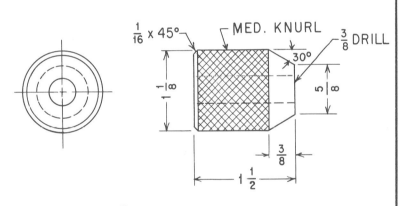

$\frac{1}{16}$ x 45° MED. KNURL $\frac{3}{8}$ DRILL

30°

② WEIGHT

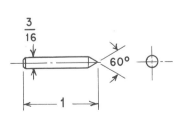

④ POINT–
DRILL ROD–HARDEN

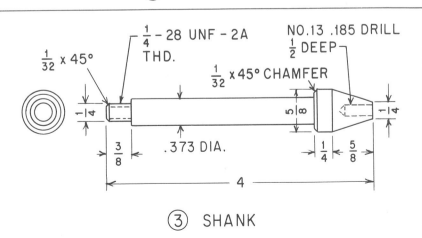

$\frac{1}{4}$ – 28 UNF – 2A THD.

NO.13 .185 DRILL
$\frac{1}{2}$ DEEP

$\frac{1}{32}$ x 45°

$\frac{1}{32}$ x 45° CHAMFER

.373 DIA.

③ SHANK

Flywheel Puller

Assignment No. 4

Make assembly and detail drawings of flywheel puller. Include parts list.

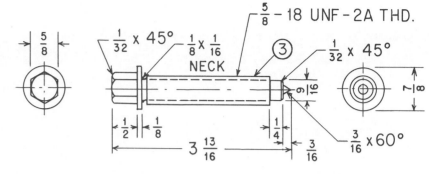

$\frac{5}{8}$ – 18 UNF – 2A THD.

$\frac{1}{32}$ x 45° $\frac{1}{8}$ x $\frac{1}{16}$ $\frac{1}{32}$ x 45°

NECK

$\frac{9}{16}$

$\frac{7}{8}$

$\frac{1}{2}$ $\frac{1}{8}$

$3\frac{13}{16}$ $\frac{1}{4}$ $\frac{3}{16}$

$\frac{3}{16}$ x 60°

③

$\frac{5}{8}$

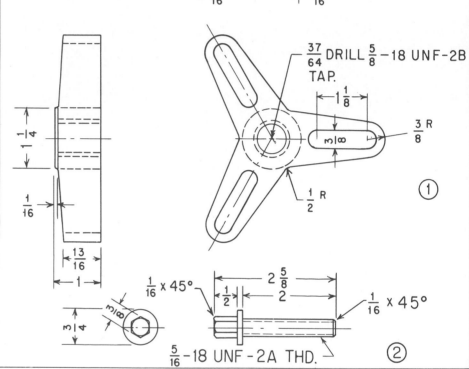

$\frac{37}{64}$ DRILL $\frac{5}{8}$ –18 UNF–2B TAP.

$1\frac{1}{8}$

$\frac{3}{8}$

$\frac{3}{8}$ R

$1\frac{1}{4}$

$\frac{1}{16}$

$\frac{1}{2}$ R

①

$\frac{13}{16}$

1

$\frac{1}{16}$ x 45° $2\frac{5}{8}$ $\frac{1}{16}$ x 45°

$\frac{1}{2}$ 2

$\frac{3}{4}$ $\frac{3}{8}$

$\frac{5}{16}$ –18 UNF –2A THD.   ②

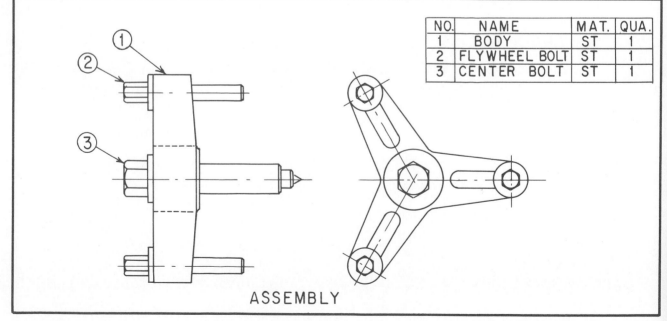

NO.	NAME	MAT.	QUA.
1	BODY	ST	1
2	FLYWHEEL BOLT	ST	1
3	CENTER BOLT	ST	1

ASSEMBLY

Parallel Clamp

Assignment No. 5

Make assembly and detail drawings of parallel clamp.
Include balloons and numbers for identification of all details.
Make parts list on assembly drawing.

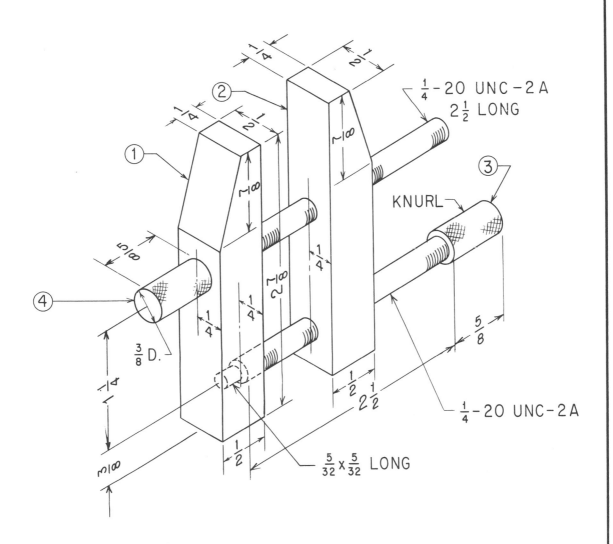

$\frac{1}{4}$ - 20 UNC - 2 A
$2\frac{1}{2}$ LONG

KNURL

$\frac{3}{8}$ D.

$\frac{1}{4}$ - 20 UNC - 2A

$\frac{5}{32} \times \frac{5}{32}$ LONG

ASSEMBLY

Wheel Puller

Assignment No. 6

Make assembly and detail drawings of the wheel puller. Scale: Full size. Include parts list and balloons.

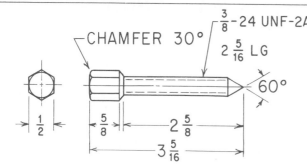

CHAMFER 30°

$\frac{3}{8}$ -24 UNF-2A

$2\frac{5}{16}$ LG

60°

$\frac{1}{2}$ $\frac{5}{8}$ $2\frac{5}{8}$

$3\frac{5}{16}$

③ SCREW–1 REQ'D–CASE HARDEN

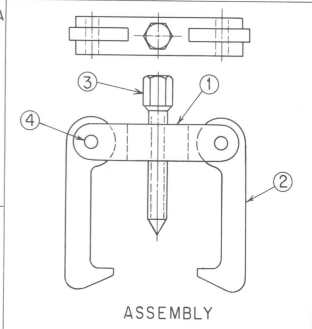

ASSEMBLY

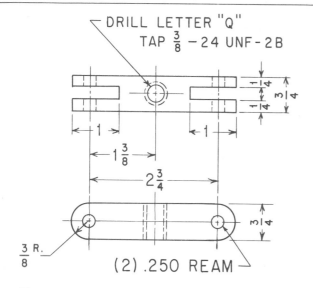

DRILL LETTER "Q"

TAP $\frac{3}{8}$ – 24 UNF-2B

$\frac{1}{4}$ $\frac{3}{4}$ $\frac{1}{4}$

1   1

$1\frac{3}{8}$

$2\frac{3}{4}$

$\frac{3}{4}$

$\frac{3}{8}$ R.

(2) .250 REAM

① CROSS BAR – 1 REQ'D

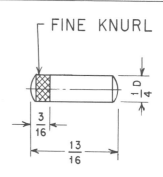

FINE KNURL

$\frac{1}{4}$ D

$\frac{3}{16}$

$\frac{13}{16}$

④ PIN – 2 REQ'D   2 x SIZE

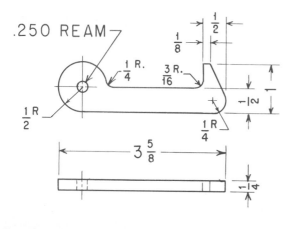

.250 REAM

$\frac{1}{2}$

$\frac{1}{8}$

$\frac{1}{4}$ R. $\frac{3}{16}$ R.

1

$\frac{1}{2}$ R.

$\frac{1}{2}$

$\frac{1}{4}$ R.

$3\frac{5}{8}$

$\frac{1}{4}$

② JAW – 2 REQ'D

No.	NAME	REQ.	MAT.
4	PIN	2	ST
3	SCREW	1	ST
2	JAW	2	ST
1	CROSS BAR	1	ST

Ball Peen Hammer

Assignment No. 7

Make assembly and detail drawings of ball peen hammer.
Scale: Full size. Include parts list.

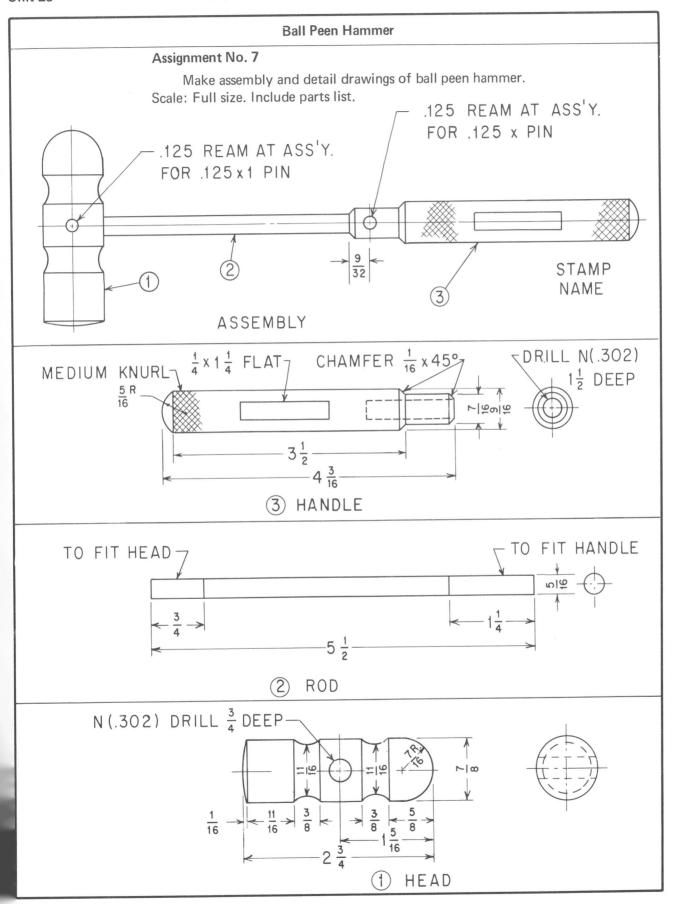

.125 REAM AT ASS'Y.
FOR .125 x 1 PIN

.125 REAM AT ASS'Y.
FOR .125 x PIN

STAMP
NAME

ASSEMBLY

MEDIUM KNURL $\frac{1}{4}$ x 1 $\frac{1}{4}$ FLAT   CHAMFER $\frac{1}{16}$ x 45°   DRILL N(.302) 1 $\frac{1}{2}$ DEEP

$\frac{5}{16}$ R

$\frac{7}{16}$ $\frac{9}{16}$

$3\frac{1}{2}$

$4\frac{3}{16}$

③ HANDLE

TO FIT HEAD

TO FIT HANDLE

$\frac{3}{4}$

$1\frac{1}{4}$

$\frac{5}{16}$

$5\frac{1}{2}$

② ROD

N(.302) DRILL $\frac{3}{4}$ DEEP

$\frac{7}{16}$ R

$\frac{11}{16}$ $\frac{11}{16}$

$\frac{7}{8}$

$\frac{1}{16}$ $\frac{11}{16}$ $\frac{3}{8}$ $\frac{3}{8}$ $\frac{5}{8}$

$1\frac{5}{16}$

$2\frac{3}{4}$

① HEAD

Binding Post

Assignment No. 8

Make assembly and detail drawings of binding post.

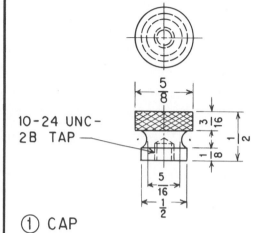

10-24 UNC-
2B TAP

① CAP

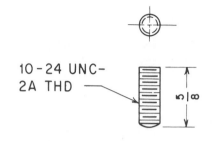

10-24 UNC-
2A THD

② STUD

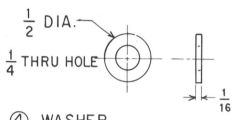

½ DIA.

¼ THRU HOLE

④ WASHER

10-24 UNC-
2A THD

⑤ SCREW

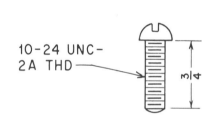

10-24 UNC-
2B TAP

3/16 D.

③ BASE

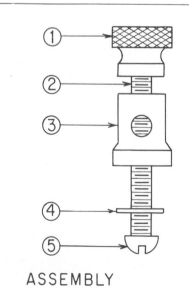

ASSEMBLY

5	SCREW	BRASS	1
4	WASHER	BRASS	1
3	BASE	BRASS	1
2	CAP SCREW	BRASS	1
1	CAP	BRASS	1
P.T.	NAME	MAT.	QUAT.

PARTS LIST

Machinist's Clamp

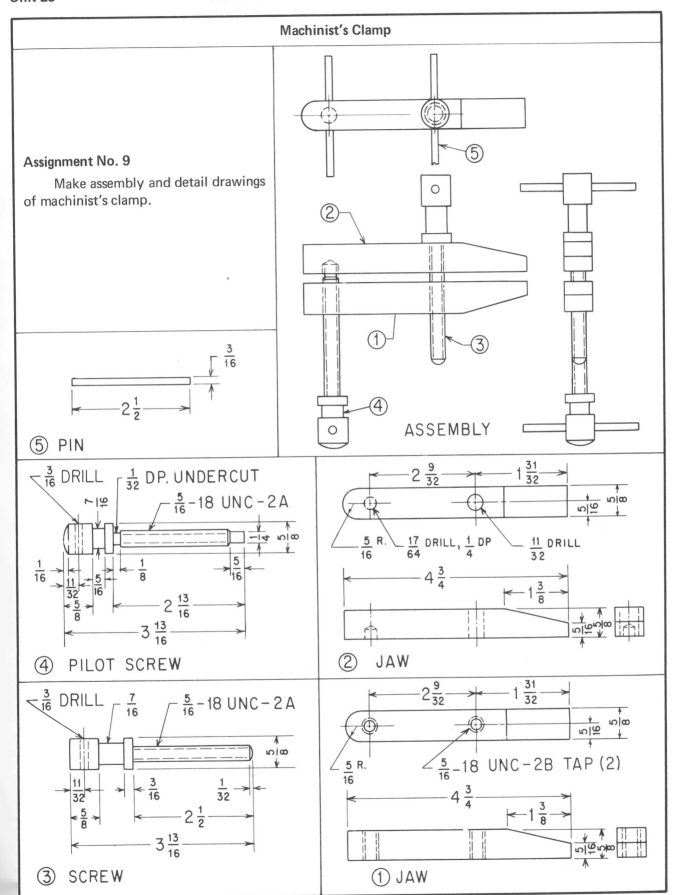

Assignment No. 9

Make assembly and detail drawings of machinist's clamp.

⑤ PIN

$\frac{3}{16}$

$2\frac{1}{2}$

ASSEMBLY

④ PILOT SCREW

$\frac{3}{16}$ DRILL $\frac{1}{32}$ DP. UNDERCUT

$\frac{5}{16}$-18 UNC-2A

$\frac{7}{16}$ $\frac{5}{8}$ $\frac{1}{4}$

$\frac{1}{16}$ $\frac{11}{32}$ $\frac{5}{16}$ $\frac{1}{8}$ $\frac{5}{16}$

$\frac{5}{8}$

$2\frac{13}{16}$

$3\frac{13}{16}$

② JAW

$2\frac{9}{32}$ $1\frac{31}{32}$

$\frac{5}{16}$ $\frac{5}{8}$

$\frac{5}{16}$ R. $\frac{17}{64}$ DRILL, $\frac{1}{4}$ DP $\frac{11}{32}$ DRILL

$4\frac{3}{4}$ $1\frac{3}{8}$

$\frac{5}{16}$ $\frac{5}{8}$

③ SCREW

$\frac{3}{16}$ DRILL $\frac{7}{16}$ $\frac{5}{16}$-18 UNC-2A

$\frac{5}{8}$

$\frac{11}{32}$ $\frac{3}{16}$ $\frac{1}{32}$

$\frac{5}{8}$

$2\frac{1}{2}$

$3\frac{13}{16}$

① JAW

$2\frac{9}{32}$ $1\frac{31}{32}$

$\frac{5}{16}$ $\frac{5}{8}$

$\frac{5}{16}$ R. $\frac{5}{16}$-18 UNC-2B TAP (2)

$4\frac{3}{4}$ $1\frac{3}{8}$

$\frac{5}{16}$ $\frac{5}{8}$

INFORMATION

It is a great help to a draftsman making an assembly drawing to have an exploded assembly drawn in isometric projection.

Here the various parts are pulled apart in the direction from which they are inserted into the assembly and in the order in which they go together, as shown on the facing page.

Exploded drawings are very helpful to the inexperienced assembler. They are useful for the purchaser of machines and also for repairmen.

PROBLEM

Make an assembly drawing of angle bracket and base. Show top, front and right side orthographic views.

Scale drawing for measurements.

INSTRUCTIONS

1. Draw border lines and title block.

2. Lay out drawing space for exploded drawing and three orthographic views. Allow space for a parts list.

3. Draw three orthographic views.

4. Use sketch on facing page for dimensions.

Making an Assembly Drawing from an Exploded Drawing

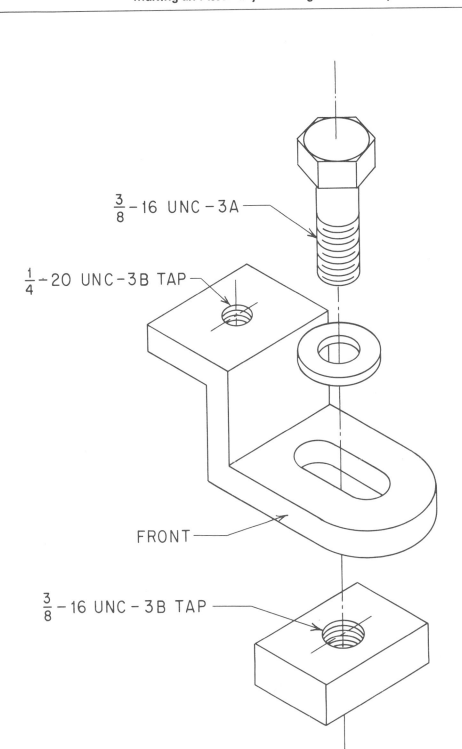

$\frac{3}{8}$ – 16 UNC – 3A

$\frac{1}{4}$ – 20 UNC – 3B TAP

FRONT

$\frac{3}{8}$ – 16 UNC – 3B TAP

Review Questions

Unit 25 review questions to be answered on a separate sheet of paper.

DIRECTIONS

For each of the numbered statements below, write the number and after it the figure, symbol, word or words which will complete the sentence. Do NOT write in the book.

1. An/a _____ drawing shows how parts are put together.
   a. perspective
   b. detail
   c. assembly
   d. isometric
   e. oblique

2. An assembly drawing has _____ or more objects.
   a. one
   b. two
   c. three
   d. four
   e. five

3. Part identification on an assembly drawing is by _____.
   a. triangles
   b. numbers
   c. arrows
   d. lines
   e. views

4. A detail drawing is a drawing of a/an _____ piece.
   a. single
   b. double
   c. sectioned
   d. oblique
   e. specified

5. An assembly drawing is a drawing of _____ or more details.
   a. two
   b. one
   c. three
   d. four
   e. five

6. A parts list is a _____ of items.
   a. blueprint
   b. list
   c. test
   d. box
   e. container

---

7. An assembly drawing is a completely _____ construction.
   a. removed
   b. separate
   c. assembled
   d. detailed

8. The detail drawing is a drawing of a _____ piece.
   a. medium
   b. small
   c. double
   d. single
   e. large

9. An assembly drawing shows how parts are _____ together.
   a. cut
   b. styled
   c. put
   d. curved
   e. detailed

10. Balloons are identifying symbols used on _____ drawings.
    a. perspective
    b. detail
    c. assembly
    d. isometric
    e. framed

VOCABULARY

Angle.—The opening or space between two lines which meet at a point.

Arc.—Any part of the circumference of a circle.

Auxiliary view.—A view which shows the true size and shape of a slanting surface. It is a projection made on a plane at an oblique angle to two or more of the principal planes of projection.

Bevel.—Inclined plane or sloping surface. To bevel is to remove a sharp edge or corner, leaving a flat sloping surface.

Bisect.—To divide into two equal parts.

Bore.—To bore is to produce an accurate round hole in metal by use of a single-point cutting tool.

Bracket.—A support in the shape of a right angle or a right triangle.

Chamfer.—To chamfer is to bevel a sharp external edge on a part.

Circle.—A plane figure enclosed within a curved boundary every point on which is equally distant from a point called the center. Also the curved surface line bounding such a figure.

Circumference.—The perimeter or boundary of a circle.

Compass.—A drafting instrument for drawing circles.

Counterbore.—To counterbore is to enlarge the diameter of a hole, usually for a sufficient depth to make room for the head of a machine screw or other fastener.

Countersink.—To countersink is to give the outer end of a drilled or bored hole an enlarged cone shape so that a flathead machine screw or other fastener can be screwed flush with the surface.

Crown.—The angle or contour of a convex surface.

Cylinder.—A sold or void surrounded by a closed curved surface and having flat, parallel and circular ends.

Degree.—1/360 of a circumference.

Diameter.—A straight line across a circle passing through the center and ending at the circumference.

Dimension.—To dimension is to give the size of an object in some units such as feet, inches, or degrees, etc.

Drill.—To drill is to produce a hole with a twist drill or other type of drill.

Elevation.—Height above a surface.

Ellipse.—A closed curve traced by a point which moves around two other points, called focii, in such a way that the sum of the distances from the focii to the moving point is always constant.

Equilateral.—A figure having all sides equal.

External.—Outside.

Fillet.—A small, rounded inner corner usually having a radius of 1/8 to 3/8 inch. It is frequently called for in metal parts where sharp inside corners are to be avoided.

Geometry.—A branch of mathematics that deals with points, lines, surfaces, and their geometrical relationships.

Helix.—A curve traced out by a point which revolves around a cylinder as it progresses axially along its length. A screw thread is a helix.

Hexagon.—A plane figure having six sides and six angles.

Hexagonal.—Six-sided.

Horizon.—The line where the earth and the sky apparently meet.

Internal.—Inside.

Interpret.—To interpret is to explain or bring out the meaning of.

Intersect.—To intersect is to cut or divide by passing through or crossing. Two lines which cross each other are said to intersect.

Key.—A small segment of metal having a square or rectangular cross section which is inserted in a keyseat to fasten a pulley, gear or other revolving member to a shaft.

Keyseat.—A longitudinal groove cut in a shaft and in the hub of a rotating member to provide space for a key to be inserted.

Lead.—The distance a threaded part moves axially with respect to a fixed mating part in one complete turn or revolution.

Lettering.—Forming letters.

Link.—To link is to join together.

Major diameter.—The largest diameter, a term usually applied to screw threads. In an external thread, it is the diameter taken over the crests of the thread. In an internal thread, it is the diameter taken at the roots of the thread.

Minor diameter.—The smallest diameter, usually applied to screw threads. In an external thread it is the diameter taken at the thread roots. In an internal thread it is the diameter taken at the thread crests.

Mount.—A supporting block.

Nut.—A small square or hexagonal block, usually made of metal, and with a threaded hole that screws onto a bolt to hold parts together.

Oblique.—Slanting. When applied to an angle it means other than 90 degrees.

Octagon.—A plane figure having eight angles and eight sides.

Octagonal.—Eight-sided.

Outside diameter.—The overall diameter.

Parallel.—Two lines, two planes, or a line and a plane are parallel if they are the same distance apart at every point.

Pentagon.—A plane figure having five sides and five angles.

Pentagonal.—Five-sided.

Perpendicular.—At right angles to.

Pitch.—The distance between the two nearest corresponding points on a screw thread measured parallel to the axis.

Pitch diameter.—On a straight thread the pitch diameter is the diameter of an imaginary cylinder, the surface of which cuts the threaded form where the width of the thread and groove are equal. Usually a diameter taken about halfway between the crest and the root. Thread tables give exact values.

Polygon.—A plane figure with several angles and sides, usually more than four.

Project.—To project is to draw or extend from one view in a straight line to another view.

Quadrilateral.—A four-sided figure.

Radius.—The distance from the center of a circle to any point on its circumference.

Ream.—To finish a hole by inserting a cutter with either straight or helical fluted teeth to scrape away the surface of the hole.

Root.—The surface of a screw thread where two sides of a thread come together. The minor diameter of an external thread may be taken at the root. The major diameter of an internal thread may be taken at the root.

Round.—To round is to smooth off a sharp edge or external corner.

Semicircle.—One half of a circle.

Spotface.—To spotface is to produce a small flat on the rounded surface of a casting or forging. It is frequently used to provide a flat seat for a washer or a nut.

Square.—A plane figure with four equal sides and four right angles.

Tangent.—Touching at one point only and not intersecting.

Tap.—A fluted tool used for cutting internal screw threads. To tap is to cut an internal thread with a tap.

Thread.—A helical groove cut around the surface of a cylinder. A screw thread is cut on screws, bolts and nuts to provide a means for their assembly in holding machine parts together.

Triangle.—A plane figure having three sides.

Trisect.—To divide into three equal parts.

Vertical.—Perpendicular to a horizontal line or surface.

INDEX